Anonymo...

A Collection of "Tails" of a hapless Health Inspector

BAZ.

To michael
"Three cups of tea!"
Stewart :)

First published in the United Kingdom in 2003.

ISBN 0-9545278-0-1

Typeset in Sabon, printed and bound in the United Kingdom by Lamberts Print & Design, Station Road, Settle, North Yorkshire, BD24 9AA.

Published by Stewart Lewis, 46 Esp Lane, Barnoldswick, BB18 5QQ.

Anonymouse

A Collection of "Tails" of a
hapless Health Inspector

Stewart Lewis

Illustrated by Barrie King

To
Christine Hilary

Contents

Foreword

THIS SET of short stories are based on my career to date as a Sanitary Inspector or as they are poshly known now – Environmental Health Officers. Most of the stories are based on "events," which have occurred throughout the width of the United Kingdom. Several, are told with a pinch of salt, or cheese! I leave the reader to choose. All characters are ficticious.

I decided to write when I was experiencing a low point in my life. My career had ended. I had to move out of my house. At that time my mother also died suddenly. I was forced into signing on for unemployment benefit and undertaking casual work. I was suffering from depression. In order to try and structure my life and time I wrote for several hours a day, joined the Citizens Advice Bureau, participated in a local art group for 50p a morning and met Barrie King who has illustrated this book. I also completed my Degree in English. This book is the result of those stygian days.

I have mentioned this episode in my life to try and explain that with support, luck and determination it is possible to recover. I have returned to my original career and moved back into my house. My depression still returns. I have reached the end of the tunnel – well almost. I hope this may be of some assistance to those who may have trod this path to know that I have been there.

No path to recovery is possible without friends. I would like to say a special thank you to those people who have been there when I needed them.

Thanks to Christine Lewis, Tania Shiffer and Catherine Sunter for proof reading and making helpful suggestions. A big thank you to John Pickles without his support and friendship some of these stories would never have been written. Also to Barrie King for the excellent cartoons.

As a last tribute. I salute Czech Mouse a small wooden creature who appears in the cartoons and in the narrative. Proof that there is that of the child in all of us, and if there is not there ought to be!

ONE

Mrs Young

ZAP! POW! ANOTHER fly hit the lethal blue light in the kitchen and was instantly incinerated. The direction of the sound bought my attention to the window where I could hear the slightly raised voices of the children at play in the school playground. I thought of asking the head cook if she wanted any more blackened flies for her currant slices but thought better of it. When I was a schoolboy it was the custom to refer to currant slices as being full of dead flies. I had already upset some poor council clerical assistant in a remote rural sub office by asking if she had sharpened her quill pen ready for the day's activities. Why are so many people in Local Government bred without the slightest degree of humour? I am not alone in these thoughts. In his diaries, Alan Clarke – a former government minister – had suffered the same misgivings when he remarked how boring some of his work and people were in the heady heights of Government.

The voices were slowly and imperceptibly rising. I glanced out of the window. Was it a fight? Whatever it was, was gathering momentum. Through the open window I could hear the sound rising and falling, very reminiscent of one of our past senior health inspector falling asleep after his lunch as though he was still working in the tropics. Alas, he is long dead but his memory lingers on. My memory of him was the very rakish hat he wore which he invariably tipped when he encountered a young lady or wished a member of the public "Good Day." It was also useful for pulling over his eyes at siesta time. Ah, such long lost times when the meaning of best value was getting a decent nap before going out for a walk around the town.

The noise, becoming more audible bought me back to reality. I could hear the chants of reed like voices, "Mrs Young, Mrs Young." Like some giant amoeba the children were flowing around a figure who as yet was not quite discernable. My attention was drawn. The continuation of the inspection would have to be put on hold whilst I waited to see what was happening. After all there could be copy for my growing number of stories.

From the tumult of young bodies I began to see one of the dinner ladies

BAZ.

or welfare assistants as they are now termed, as the centre of attention. Would the view reveal some young brat who had been trying to kiss the girls, or more likely in these modern times been trying to extort some protection racket money from his peers. Perhaps he was stealing a mobile phone. Should I call Jack Hay down hot foot to serve an immediate curfew order on the minion. Worse still if he was the son of an asylum seeker he would be sent back from where he had come and of course his vouchers deducted as payment for the homeward trip.

By now I had been joined by the head cook who looked on, rubbing her hands on some oven cloth. She reminded me, strangely, of a mechanic except she had flour on her hands rather than oil, but the stance was the same. After a few moments of thought she declared, "Why it's Mrs Young our dinner lady, oops I mean our welfare assistant. What ever is going on?" Together we looked on, I clutched my notebook and she her oven cloth – the symbolism of our professions, except, I thought to myself, she produces a tangible commodity.

By now the circle had grown and Mrs Young was central to the crowd of bawling youngsters. The noise had grown and was reaching fever pitch. Mrs Young though, was a model of tranquillity. In her hand was a football. "Spoilsport," I thought, she has confiscated the ball. Then Mrs Young carefully, almost with reverence, placed the ball on the puddled playground surface, taking great care to brush away several Pokemon bubble gum wrappers. As she backed away from the ball, still looking at it with a demonic expression, I could see a small figure about five yards away from her crouching between a pile of clothes which were quite clearly a set of makeshift goal posts. For what seemed an eternity, a silence settled over the playground, everyone was frozen in time. I was sure that even the birds had stopped singing and were watching.

From the corner of my eye I could see old "Figurine," the maths teacher, watching from his study window over hawk like glasses, his abacus suspended in mid calculation and his mortar board tipping precariously in such a manner that at any moment Newton's law of gravity would come into effect. In a far corner of the playground "Menace" the playground bully was about to thump some wimp who no doubt went to ballet classes, or something else as ephemeral, but his hand remained poised skywards, suspended. The caretaker's cat sat mesmerised missing his one and only chance to consume a mouse who lay whiskers quivering beneath its poised darkened shadow.

The world had stopped, all except for Mrs Young who appeared to have turned and was rushing towards the stationary ball. Her apron flowed like a Dervish rider as she approached the ball. I was sure "Figurine" would be working out the velocity of Mrs Young's run, but the calculation would be incorrect for a sudden glimpse of black knitted thigh – cor – as it retracted before striking the spherical object, would have plunged his abacus into disarray. Figurine had long since had an equilateral passion for our welfare assistant. To him black knitted thigh or glimpse thereof was equal to the angle of passion. Quod erat demonstrandum. No doubt that the question would be posed at the upper sixths, who were probably more interested in all matters sexual than some obtuse mathematical equation. Smack! Ball and foot hit the ball in one joyful motion worthy of the beautiful game. Mrs Young rose into the air, her shooting leg stretched out like some of the famous shots of Bobby Charlton – but with more hair – in mid flight. The young goalkeeper dived more in gesture than hope and lay sprawled on the playground surface. The ball whizzed past him and cannoned off the wall behind and rebounded hitting his bemused head which for a second time re-inspected the playground tarmac.

A huge cheer rent the playground. The air pressure so great that

"Figurines" mortar board toppled even more over his forehead. Those birds watching the spectacle shuddered in the updraft. Mrs Young leaped skywards, her outstretched arms nearly reaching the ruffled birds, and ran toward her adoring supporters, pulling her pinny over her face as all good professionals now do, she ran berserk around the playground. Hordes of pupils hugged her and offered their pet frogs, Pokemon cards or catapults to show their appreciation. Their hero, their scoring dinner lady, the Maradona of Barnoldswick. Mrs Young had scored the only penalty of her life but what a penalty. Mrs Young Ra! Ra! Ra! Mrs Young, we'll support you evermore.

Amidst the tumult a lone cat sat nursing its wounded pride and wondering why the mouse so big and plump had become a very hard shadow... Time, had begun again.

TWO

The Queen of Ciabatta and the Tardis

READERS MAY OR may not know the following, Ciabatta is a type of moist Italian bread made with olive oil. It is also known as "the slipper" because of its shape. A Tardis is an old blue London police box inhabited by Doctor Who which travelled in time and was much larger inside than it appeared externally. Doctor Who was a mad professor who fought with daleks in a TV series. The scene is set in a large university city in the north of England.

I walk up the main drag with my food inspection bag looking like some waif in search of either a job or accommodation. Around me are thousands of students who appear to be looking younger and younger as the days and years progress. I observe the predisposition to the bare midriff of the women, often a small jewel sparking from somewhere in the region of the navel. I must be getting old for my thoughts are that a bare midriff must give you a chill and to the dangers of having your body pierced in that particular region of your anatomy. I had always been wary of this but last year I had seen a slide show by an eminent professor on the subject of body piercing and some of the sights and infection were suitably horrendous. The eminent professor gave his talk in that characteristic modem of the English professor using self depreciation and dry humour when explaining the more gory details.

I glance at my map and check that I am in the correct location. Yes, I am here. A small sandwich shop. Should not take long. Yes, I know it is lunch time but now I am a city inspector I must be firm and forceful. Targets must be reached or I will be sent back from whence I had emerged. My mind cast back to a formidable boss nicknamed "The Czar" who despite global warming, could still occasionally have a very severe cold front. Rumour had it that he had once looked at an additional cup of tea an inspector was drinking when he should have been out and caused the temperature of the brew to fall several degrees. I am unable to confirm if this was Celsius or

Fahrenheit, and the windows did not burst open and lightening flash. That would be too fanciful!

Inside the sandwich shop there appeared to be thousands of munching students and desperate people shouting out in some form of Yorkshire Italian to come pay their money here, there, or anywhere as long as they got paid and got out of the door to allow some more bare midriff students to come in. I explained who I was. A quick look round the back and I would be off. "You must go to the top says Dino." I follow him to the top of the building where I pass floor upon floor of people making sandwiches. On the top floor, Italian bread is being baked, cut up and buttered. In another room ingredients are stored. On the next floor a whole phalanx of women are busy making the sandwiches. They laugh and sing in a strange voice. "Ah these are my Brazilian girls." Says Dino with a wide embrace of his arms as though he is singing some aria in Milan. His chest swells and his eyes widen as he exclaims, "and this one – lips pursed – she is my special Queen of Ciabbaticca." A doe eyed girl looks up at him and smiles a look of sunshine and Brazilian beach. She is so adept at sandwich production that it is an art form and a joy to watch her fluid movements as she caresses the butter on to the bread and exchanges looks with Dino, the meaning of which I will leave to your imagination.

As we speak, an Iranian came in. Or rather his bright red scarf comes in before him. "Prego!" Dino exclaims voice sote dolce. "This is Mustafa. He is an illegal immigrant from Iran." Dino then collapses with laughter as he laughs at his own joke. Mustafa looks at him and smiles. The international language of hope. He is radiantly happy to be working and smiles at me and I shake his hand. I remember the flash of his white teeth contrasting with the red neck scarf he was wearing.

From one of the production rooms I looked down on the busy street below. Who would have thought that the bustle of the street was equally matched inside this Tardis? I counted six rooms plus a basement, all producing international sandwiches, the fillings of which varied from day to day, depending on what the Queen of Ciabatica wanted to make.

Dino explained to me that the firm produces a thousand sandwiches a day. Compared to the rest of the staff, he and his several partners are old enough to be classed as dinosaurs but they somehow keep the place running. He offers me a special sandwich and a super coffee as I write my report. On the whole, it was very good considering the age of the premises and the amount of sandwich production. He does though, have a problem with some mice next door who appear to be nesting in some rubbish. He has seen them scuttling about. He is also worried about something else he has observed. Occasionally, the mice appear to stagger, sometimes roll onto their backs and shake their legs about in the air. Is this normal? I explain that I have not heard of this before and will look in to it as soon as possible. I struggle out of the Tardis and emerge into the sunlight. From high above I can hear the sound of a samba band playing and the Brazilian girls singing.

I still have some time and decide to call next door and try to find out about the problem with the rodents.

Next door is somewhat more salubrious. It has a receptionist who seems intent on leaving the building for her lunch break. She asks me to sit down on some ridiculous style of sofa, which is extremely low, whilst she gets a member of staff. I sit or rather fall on to the sofa and amuse myself. By and by a female member of the species emerges and comes and sits down next to me. The slit in her skirt indicates that she has a leg which extends above her knee caps. I move slightly to one side of the sofa to allow her some room. Now all of a sudden I am seeing the view of her legs from ground level. I have moved over and forgot that I was on the end of a sofa with out an arm and of course went completely of the edge. What a fool. I scramble up and try to regain my dignity. Nonchalantly she asks if I am OK but I'm sure she is dying to run away and laugh. She remains passive. I'm certain that if a bomb was dropped she would be still there. I explain why I am visiting and request if I may have a quick look around the building to see what is going on.

This is a wonderful job for nosy parkers! Under the law of the United Kingdom you are able to demand entry to premises to check for things called nuisances which may affect the public health of the general population. Now what, you might ask, is a nuisance? Well, according to some very old case law, it is anything so ordinary which would affect the average citizen who might so happen to be riding on the Clapham omnibus. So reader, if you happen to be riding on the Clapham omnibus and suffer a nuisance give your friendly Environmental Health Officer a ring and ask to speak to the Chief Inspector of Nuisances. Rumour has it that in some rural areas this species still exists and keeps some minority industry in business producing quill pens and blotting paper. "So," I ask, "what do you produce here?"

"Vodka jelly." She replies with an air of supreme disdain. Whether the

BAZ.

disdain is directed at the product or myself I will leave to your imagination. Oh dear! Again I am completely out of my depth here. "What on earth are vodka jelly's?" I ask. "Hang on." She replies, and rises from the sofa in a fluid movement which would cause the driver of the Clapham omnibus to have a controlled collision with other motorised vehicles upon the Queen's highway. She emerges with a small red phial and a plastic sword. Phial of jelly, sword and body again smoothly make contact with the sofa. She holds the small plastic phial with one hand and in the other she removes the plastic lid. Then she inserts the plastic sword to run around the sides of the container and then gives the bottom a quick tap. Before I can fall off the sofa again she has downed the contents in one. She throws the discarded container into the bin and appears to disappear into the sofa. From the depths of wherever she is, her voice dreamily tells me that there is a special ingredient from South America which stops you shuddering as the contents reach your stomach. I reflect that I will be shortly going to South America and may find the source of the elixir. Perhaps I could give a paper to a conference on the subject.

So down to business. I had come to see if I could sort out the problem with the mice about which the inhabitants of the Tardis were complaining. I can not tell them who the complainants are as that had to remain confidential. Slowly and slightly unsteadily she raises herself from the depths of the sofa and, once on her feet, beckons me into the inner sanctum of the establishment.

The insides of the building were as pristine and boring as the receptionist, not a hair out of place. Row upon row of different coloured containers stretched before my eyes. I had a poke around and found nothing. I decided to head for base and try my slipper sandwich. The mice and their mysterious affliction would have to be solved another day.

Back at base I sat back with my thoughts and a brew. Not though, before making tea for everyone else. Unfortunately I had now become saddled with the name of "Sid The Teaboy." Oh well, such is life. Anyone for tea?

So time went on. The Tardis produced sandwiches, the vodka jellies were consumed and I took a professional course on tea making which, as part of the new "Investors In People" award, was deemed to be an extremely worthy cause; it encouraged the interpersonal flagging up of inter-departmental matters at a grassroots level or even root and branch.

Then one day, trouble. The mice had been seen again, this time performing what a late night student had said appeared to be a collective samba which ended with them all laying on their backs with their feet in the air. Now this fact could have been attributed to drunken students' antics but local authority officers must now bear in mind the human rights of the complainant and deal with the complaint promptly. This meant obtaining a warrant to get in to the vodka factory as the premises had closed for the day. A glance at our list of magistrates gave us several options as to whom to contact. Justice Fyfes caught my eye and also the little note at the side of his name stating, "Ring before going. Has a tendency to play games with his children in which he appears as a fruit ghost wearing a white gown and a bunch of bananas on his head."

"Never." I said to my colleague. "It's a joke."

"No." Said he. "The social services were on the case several months ago. Evidently the kids had been writing about the matter in their school essays and one of the jobsworth teachers had reported the matter to the thought police. So beware. For the sake of curiosity I choose Justice Fyfes.

In great trepidation I knocked on the door. A sturdy figure opened it and beckoned me in. I explained the situation about the drunken mice and he gave the matter his utmost attention before asking me to swear an oath of allegiance to king and country before granting the warrant. I was just thinking that this could not be the very same judge when, with the force of a high wind in Jamaica, a small boy rushed in through the door complete with white sheet and bananas exclaiming, "Daddy daddy let's play fruit ghost!" With warrant in hand, I was propelled out of the door faster than the boy had come in. As the door closed I was sure I could hear supernatural squeals.

So back to the premises. On hand are Reacham Cracem who is a locksmith, a member of the law and myself. "Cor blimey!" Said the constable. "There're going bananas round the back, mice all over the place like its a bleeding carnival!" A quick shine of his Moriarty police issue lantern revealed some mighty strange goings on. I have never quite seen so many mice completely legless. Clearly there was a major problem some where for their numbers were growing by the minute.

Cracem did his duty and we were in. Of course I had to go in first. If there was trouble the law would send for reinforcements but this would only be after I had, no doubt, been bitten to death. Cracem sat down, opened his flask and started to read the paper for this was as far as he went. He would of course secure the place when we left. He was on something like double time plus strange duty bonus coupled with a full moon allowance. The lantern beam – don't forget, reader, the police are going retro to appeal to us members of the public – sliced through the darkened interior. The beams refracted from the various vodka colours and gave the building a strange hue. It would have been easier to turn the light on but then the story would never be as good and I would not be able to tell the tale of the police lantern. We could see nothing. The building was as it was the last time I visited it, not a hair out of place. By this time were were becoming perplexed. Then we saw a door behind a small alcove. Carefully we prised it open, or should I say, Cracem did, for it was within his demarkation that he was only allowed to open and close one extra door. He was delighted in an extra bonus which he had informed us might allow him to retire early. He had then planned to sell his services back to the council for double the price. It was something to do with a concept called "Best Value." He muttered.

All was revealed. An overpowering smell of undiluted vodka hit us. There must be a leak. All around our feet were the remains of broken vodka jellies and the cheeky buggers, the mice, were there just eating it as though they did not see or care about us. Evidently one did at last see us. Instinct got the better of it and it made a dash for the door but missed, hit the brick wall and bounced off it, its eyes swimming around. Once one had ran, the rest followed and a tide of drunken mice ran over our feet and out into the street where they appeared to be having a mass samba dance.

"Make the most of it, we've found you out." I shouted at the dancing mob. I was clearly affected by the vodka fumes.

There was little left for us to do. Holmes left to attend a press conference of the new Sherlock style cloak, very PC. Cracem was left happily repairing the locks whilst listening to the sound of some ghastly music.

As I left for home I passed Justice Fyfes mansion. A silhouette in one of the upper window reveals a shapeless figure with what appeared to be a bunch of bananas on his head. Suddenly the new fangled mobile 'phone rang. A member of the public had been woken up by a locksmith singing some Brazilian song at the top of his head and doing the samba. My attention was suddenly drawn to a slight movement on my passenger seat. I looked down. There sprawled a merry mouse complete with seat belt who winked at me and raised his bottle.

THREE

Hear All. See All. Say Nowt

"ER... CAN I have a screwdriver and a hammer please?"

I tentatively addressed a receding hairline, the only sign of my senior's face hidden behind the *Farmers Guardian*. Was the cause of the hairline either the fall in livestock prices – even in 1976? Or the inability to arrange for a free transfer of this wayward turbulent young sanitary inspector – myself!

In the pause which followed between the ingestion of the thought and the lowering of the newspaper, the realisation flashed through my mind that I had learnt more about the price of hay, proven – animal feed – and sheep as frantic debates raged in the office over the doom that was overtaking the farming fraternity. Such tales of woe were matched only by the sounds of exasperation as yours truly required extracting from the jaws of an irate councillor or member of the public over some job which had gone horribly wrong. One such occasion was when a councillor who owned a huge black dog came in to the office to complain about another huge black dog barking. I do not know how it happened but he ended up getting the letter requesting that he keep his dog silent. That did not go down well! He had been "Lewised," as a colleague who has a love of the horse racing fraternity would say. This colleague loves nothing better than sitting on her arm chair side pretending it is a horse wearing a riding helmet, completed with whip, glass of claret and a copy of Horse and Hound pretending to ride over over hill and dale. I must admit I am prone to such mishaps. But then I admit them, whilst others hide beneath their blank exteriors.

The once proud *Farmers Guardian* was now a crumpled heap among the detritus of butties, snap box and old shag tobacco. His attention drawn, a hush descended upon the office.

"What's young Lewis done now?"... For some reason I have always been referred to as young Lewis, but that's another story. As our office clock methodically ticked away I began. "Well... it's like this..."

I had occasion to visit a property in Trafalgar, Lancashire, the reason for

which is lost in the annals of time.

Reaching the property I used the distinctive knock which had been part of my training. No reply. Do I go back for any early brew or go around t'back as they say here? Being keen, I sauntered around up the back street and rattled the yard gate. This is a good method of checking for any unwanted canines lurking within the confines of the yard. In an era when folk still often use outside closets, the rattle of the gate will also indicate if anyone is using the facility. Giving another tap on the door and getting no reply I peeped through the back window. Through faded, yellowing lace curtains I saw a recumbent figure slumped in an old armchair. Further knocks on the window succeeded only in causing some startled spiders to rush for cover, afraid that their sojourn of lazily spinning cobwebs may be rudely shattered. There was no response. More knocking and lace curtains behind windows up and down the street all begin to twitch and who knows how many more spiders, who had hurt no one, may have tumbled to an untimely death.

Brushing the remnants of dust from my hands I decided to telephone for assistance from the hair dressing salon next door, long before unisex was invented. The thought of entering this hive of women encased in strange hoods with the ever present smell of hair lacquer alarmed me. Not only would I smell of something entirely different from old shag tobacco and thus give rise to even more ribbing, I would fail to answer those amazing frank questions such as, "Where are you going for your holidays? Going out tonight?" With the ever present threat of being questioned, or worse still, being grabbed by my flowing locks and being given a blue rinse, I side stepped the driers, avoided a well aimed spray, slipped on a loose curler and just made it to the telephone. Just making myself heard above the sound of Radio One I 'phoned the local constabulary.

Two tone lights flashing, the officer arrived, peeked through the window and requested "sonny" – myself to hold the door handle. Crash. The door flew open and before I could utter Edwin Chadwick* a size ten shiny regulation boot made contact with the door. I envisaged the spiders getting tin helmets and applying for a rate reduction, being extremely fed up with further shocks to the routine of their day. Perhaps they would head off on their holidays to a more peaceful abode. Was there a Club 18 to 30 Arachnid or even one for the more mature spider, "Spinaweb?"

Brushing aside more cobwebs we entered the room. It was like a scene from a wild west movie. Amidst a cloud of dust, the door was hanging at a crazy angle on its remaining hinge. A scene from Dickens confronted us, everything thread bare including the figure. Was this my first death?

The room lay before me. A solitary place was set for one on a table with no cloth but covered by yesterdays newspaper: another lonely meal, the teapot steaming idly. The clock on the mantelpiece stopped at ten to three. I wondered if there would be time enough for tea. The fireplace contained a small fire with a pitiful flame reflecting the apparent lack of life in the room. I imagined a mouse standing in front of the fire, toasting fork in hand, giving up on the inadequate fire. It would have to make do with cold bread and cheese. Perhaps along with the spiders, it might call it a day and head for pastures or cheese anew. Slowly my gaze fixed on the figure slumped in the chair. The hairs at the back of my neck which had escaped a blue rinse rose as, imperceptibly, the figure twitched. Slowly an arm rose, followed by a strange alternating whistling noise. I suddenly became aware that the noise was coming from the figure, and not from the constable's radio. As though in slow motion a hand was being raised towards his right ear. In a manner matching his arm movements his head rose to meet my gaze and then to Mr Size Ten.

"Eh lad, I were nappin' and t'bugger dropped out," he said replacing his hearing aid.

Before I could utter a single word Size Ten had legged it, forgetting his two tone lights.

Alone, old man and young lad looked at each other, the silence only broken by the creaking of a door in the wind, and several spiders with size ten boots legging it, followed by a forlorn mouse with a piece of cheese wrapped in a red cloth attached to a pole!

Edwin Chadwick. One of the great public health reformers. Born in 1800 and died in 1890. Chadwick argued that disease was spread by the physical conditions of housing which was linked to the well being of the inhabitants. Chadwick's agitation lead to the introduction of the Public Health Act of 1848. Although it is 150 years ago since the Act was introduced, Hansard the journal of Parliament has shown that many of the issues of the time bear many strong relationships with contemporary concerns.

FOUR

Wanted For The War Effort

DEAR READER.

Before this story can be read and understood, it is necessary to know a little history of the United Kingdom. During the Second World War 1939-1945 there was a shortage of metal to produce aircraft, guns, ammunition and bombs. It was also the custom for aluminium saucepans to be collected and melted down to produce lightweight parts for aircraft. It is still a lasting legacy that if you look at small walls around houses even to this day you can still see the holes where those railings once were. At the time of writing I am informed that the metal was in fact never used. It was a psychological ploy to make people think they were contributing to the war effort.

Now that you are in possession of this historic information read on, but bear in mind that our story occurred in the 1980's.

Way back in the heady days of my career I was based in Trafalgar Lancashire. A small town renamed after the historic battle of Trafalgar. Our office was based on a corner of Hardy Road, a busy highway giving an ideal vantage point to watch the world go by. As young inspectors there was the opportunity to look at various fanciable young girls to-ing and fro-ing from the solicitor's offices which surrounded us. One of our pranks was often to tap on the window as one such female passed below and duck away from the window. The result was that any poor unsuspecting colleague was left gawping and severely embarrassed whilst we disappeared and the young female looked up. Perhaps in our more politically correct times I should include that there may have been some inspectors who looked at fanciable blokes. Oh dear the list could continue for ever!

This was not very professional conduct but the work got done, people were happy and "stress" was an unknown word. But do I speak a lie. I am of course speaking from the perspective of past youth with no mention of the more senior staff who daily had to save the likes of myself and others from their misdemeanours. Grundy our senior inspector, had aged severely since I had arrived. But, I consoled myself with the thought that it could have been the problems of the farming fraternity. I remember with fondness having exciting rides in his mini, competing for space with a quantity of straw bales and other farming implements. The car would often have that homely aroma of old shag tobacco and the sweet smell of livestock. Often, when arriving at our destination, it was necessary to brush off the odd bit straw and, by heck, it did itch if they got down yer back!

So today was as per usual a normal start. Our old boss Top Cat had as been in. He used to be in the navy during the war and marched up and down the office shouting out instructions as though he was on the bridge of a destroyer, making sure that yours truly was under control. At least his tirade was less than when the notorious "Burglar Bonham" – another story – got changed in his office and forgot to rescue his trousers. The result was that he came in the following morning with a peg over his nose and holding the aforesaid garments as far as his arms could extend, muttering expletives about his office being used as a depository for Oxfam. Top Cat, in moments of reflective calm, would often tell us stories of the sea and use cricketing analogies like "close of play" to denote the end of the day. I'm afraid I never went far in his estimation as when he once asked me about the cricket score I said, "I'm not sure but I think the nightwatchman is about to bat." I later reflected that this person "Nightwatchman" played in a lot of games, and thought no more about it!

On one occasion I was summoned in to his office to be asked if I had at any time thought about a move to another local authority. TC said there was a nice little council over on the coast and would I like to move there? In my naivety I replied that I was quite happy. As I left the plush office elegantly lined with some flock wallpaper I would hear a very distinctive sobbing. TC did one day offer me a pearl of wisdom in that I should work for a larger authority. I never took his advice until I was forced into such a move. Looking back I should have followed his advice. A big city has more to offer and keeps me young in heart and mind and of course more copy for stories. Poor old TC, you were right.

Grundy our senior inspector was given a complaint relating to dampness from which a householder had been suffering due to an alleged piece of missing troughing – guttering – from next door. A normal complaint. However, this one was difficult and not to be trusted with a mere mortal like myself. The house in question belonged to a well know eccentric who moved around the streets of Trafalgar as though he was on manoeuvres with

BAZ.

the army engaged in street combat. In fact we had all seen him from our vantage point of our office. He would move down the street with his back to the wall, his hands feeling the surface. As he reached a corner he would stop for a second or two and then cautiously peer around the corner revealing only his head, which was suitably attired with an old mining helmet complete with lamp. Once this manoeuvre was complete he would turn the corner quickly for fear of attracting enemy fire and carry on as normal before until he reached home. It was rumoured that the said gentleman had also got an armoured car parked in his rear yard. I am unable to confirm this fact.

Now it was well known that this particular gentleman could not be approached and spoken to in the normal manner. It would require an especially tactful officer to undertake the necessary enquiry. Who better than our wise leader who sat puffing on his pipe, deep in thought as to how to solve the problem. As the tobacco fumes filtered through the office, Grundy sighed and set off on his course of action. He had just seen our subject approaching the office and took his chance. Our venue offered us the ideal chance to see our leader in action.

As our subject approached, we could see our Grundy inches away in a similar position back against the wall being told to stay close in case of enemy fire and to turn the corner quickly which, of course, he did. What a sight they presented, a man complete with mining helmet being pursued by a bearded inspector smoking a pipe and wearing some sort of weather beaten jacket fastened with an old bit of baling twine. Eventually the two disappeared and we awaited the outcome.

At long last our Grundy appeared, his jacket smeared with the soot from buildings and the odd hole, no doubt from one or two stray bullets! Some splatter marks looked serious but on closer investigation showed themselves to be some examples of the famous Lancashire mushy pea. He sat down, knocked his pipe out and in the manner of a thousand fireside thoughts muttered, through slurps of Yorkshire tea, and tobacco smoke, "T'old bugger said he couldn't get t'troughing as it were wanted for t'war effort."

Strenuous efforts were made via the social services department to persuade our friend that plastic had been invented and the problem was solved. I'm not sure about the armoured car, but there are many stories yet to be told!

FIVE

Water Water Everywhere

BY 'ECK THA knows it's reet champion t'have water supply to sup and flush kasi wi'. Translation – Goodness gracious me it is really good to have a decent water supply to have a drink and flush the toilet with.

It stands to reason that the wondrous ways of water cause much tribulation and are often the subject of investigation by the Sanitary Inspector, or what is known in our enlightened times as the Environmental Health Officer. We in this country are in some ways blessed in that our complaints are often related to supply and the means of disposing of that supply, once used, in a safe manner. Many countries are denied that basic right and indeed it is argued that in the future wars instead of being fought over oil will be fought over the access to water.

Many years ago, as a fledgling inspector, I had to go on a visit with my senior, also called Stewart. This had led to quite a lot of confusion back at the office. The problem being solved by calling myself Ian, my middle name. The subject of our visit was a rather scruffy man at his home in Clogg Heads Lancashire. Stewart was more experienced and was showing "a young 'un" the ropes.

To my surprise Stewart called, in rather blunt terms, the person's home and demeanour "mucky" and told him in no uncertain terms to clean his house and personage up. We would be back the next day to ensure both house and person were in a clean and sanitary fashion so as not to be causing a smell nuisance to his neighbours. I seem to remember that the scruffy man was a herbalist and had scattered throughout his kitchen many varied herbs of which he claimed he could cure all manner of ills. Perhaps, looking back, I should never have embarked upon the role of Nuisance Inspector as I felt my colleague had been a little harsh on him, and after all, wasn't the subject of herbal cures of a much greater interest to public health? Anyway I digress. Off we went to our next complaint thinking no more about the situation.

The next day arrived. Before we could go to the house, there was the

daily briefing on the state of Renie's car. Renie was our sole secretarial support and virtually controlled the entire office from her solid oak desk. It was a commonly held belief that her car was held together with baling twine and chewing gum. Every morning you could be sure that something had dropped off it since the previous day. Our task was usually to locate the part and to tell her if it was important. This scenario every morning usually consisted of several of us standing around the car with an ancient manual trying to work out the front from the back. The escape of smoke and loud reports as Renie set of for home at the end of the day revealed that we had guessed right. We would sigh with relief as the car disappeared into the distance veering from left to right and bumping up and down over the cobbled street

After this discussion we set off on our visit and reaching the property, Stewart and myself marched up the garden path with a zeal, after all we were the protectors of the health of the public. As the student and, of course, being in deference to my experienced colleague I held back to observe his skill, making notes for future assignments. With a rat-a-tat-tat upon the door our leader demanded entry. No response. Another knock, this time more demonstrative, the door frame quivering and the sound echoing off the other nearby houses. Soon, I thought, the whole street would be out and then we would be for it as we fielded complaints of why Mrs Scroggines' bin had not been emptied and why the corner shop continued to put rat or mice into those pies which sold like hot cakes.

I reflect after twenty five years I have never once found a rat or a mouse in any fridge or, come to think of it, any pie. I have, though, seen a very dead cockroach which had the misfortune to be crushed by a bread loaf that had been placed into a baking tin prior to baking, and then incinerated. But no vermin much to my utter disappointment. I once reflected this point sadly to a shop proprietor and was nearly lynched.

There seemed a pause which lasted an eternity. What would my leader do? As if from afar a voice suddenly hailed us, "oi you sonny," I cringed since I was usually the only sonny. This time the voice was directed at my colleague and was coming from the upstairs window out of which the subject of our visit leaned. We both looked up and in so doing came face to face with liquid effluent on its downward spiral. The inevitable occurred and made contact with my colleague's face looking skywards. His remaining words were lost in a splutter of sound as effluvia and personage fused into one. I, of course, escaped unscathed being a suitably respectful distance away. A hasty retreat was made back to HQ which was in the good old days, equipped with a kitchen complete with drying facilities and a telephone exchange salvaged from the trenches of the First World War. Our kitchen also possessed a working oven on which lunch was prepared. It was not unusual to return to the office and smell the delightful lunch which was being prepared. Stacked along the shelves of the kitchen were bottles of old Tom's wine brewing jars merrily gurgling away.

Back in the office Jim, the rat catcher – well nowadays they are called pest control operatives – nearly had a heart attack as our bedraggled inspector came in dripping puddles on the linoleum floor, his 1960's anorak sodden. The laughter rose as the tale unfolded. Renie, the only master of the antiquated telephone system, had cast her car manual to one side and was choking with laughter. It was touch and go who to watch. Jim looked as though he was having convulsions as he sat doubled on his chair, his flat cap dangerously close to falling off and revealing an aspect of his anatomy that even his wife had never seen. The trusty dog, Rex, a veteran rat and mouse catcher, careered up and down the linoleum clad floor skidding at each end as he flew after biscuits which Jim threw to him in between convulsions. What any person calling into the office would have thought I dread to think. Come to think of it, the only people who seemed to call were the hard of hearing in those days as we used to dish out free hearing aid batteries.

Soon all was restored to order, or what passed for order as the boss, who we affectionately called "The Curate" due to his reverential tones and manner, woke up hearing the noise in the next office and came in requesting a cup of tea. No mug, a proper bone china cup and saucer, and his afternoon digestive suggestive biscuit.

The laughter settled in to an air of suppressed mirth. Rex sat exhausted chewing a biscuit, the rat catcher had re-adjusted his cap and slurped tea from the saucer. Renie was again lost in her car manual. I of course, being the studious type was reading the current best seller on how to be a better inspector. Even "The Curate" allowed himself a small smirk in between gentle sips of Earl Grey, not from the saucer. As his head tilted back in gentle thoughts he, no doubt, reflected with some degree of satisfaction that it was not yours truly causing the problem – for once!

You may ask did the scruffy man clear up the house? Well maybe he did and then again maybe he didn't for it has no bearing on the events told!

SIX

Passages Through Time

IN MY WORK as an Sanitary Inspector, Nuisance Inspector, Public Health Officer and now Environmental Health Officer – I wonder what I will be called in the future? – I have received complaints from members of the public about smells. These can be far ranging. A dead rat or mouse beneath the occupants floor – no, not in their food – the poor old rodent having eaten some new fangled gourmet poison, and knowing it is about to die, crawls to a convenient warm spot to spend its final moments. This is usually, reader, near your hot water pipe which is hidden beneath the floor and usually extremely difficult to get at. That is when the plumber at last visits, sucks in his breath between his teeth, scratches his head, pushes back his cap and thinks pound notes or even Euro's. In the meantime the dead rodent slowly cooks at a rate that is not recommended by the Food Standards Agency until you notice that it is not yesterdays dinner that is off.

To avoid this scenario the advice is to use an old fashioned "Little Nipper Trap," which can be purchased from the local hardware shop, if one still exists in the area and, with the important caveat that you are able to remove the shrink wrap that everything seems to come wrapped up in these days

So, off to investigate the said smell, nose appropriately attuned after a suitable brew. A visit to the complainant's house reveals that the smell appears to be coming from next door. It is absolutely awful and is drowning out the smell of his freshly brewed coffee. I am offered a sample – not of the smell – but his latest brew. He apologizes that it is Nicaraguan. Not wishing to embarrass my self more than usual, I do not ask about the merits of Nicaraguan coffee but simply smile and accept – I seem to do a lot of that now – our coffee maker disappears into the South American Jungle to grind the coffee. As I sit contemplating the Guardian newspaper and resist the temptation to have a quick go on the pan pipes left on the table. I get a whiff. Not of the coffee but the smell. Even by my own standards a visit to the source is called for. After a discussion on the differing merits of coffee beans, it is time to investigate. Before entering the suspected property I reach for my handy baling twine to tie up the bottom of my trousers in order to prevent fleas jumping up my legs. This is a handy tip I have learnt from Jim, our rat catcher, who though having no academic qualifications has more practical knowledge than the entire health profession put together. Crash! I suddenly see the patterns of the Complainants carpet up close from a horizontal position. South American, I think. I really must remember to cut that baling twine!

I knock on the suspect's door, not too loudly as I would really rather go back for another coffee or even learn to tie baling twine in a more proficient way. I have a quick peep through the letter box. I have learned to peep carefully from a suitable distance as the odd walking stick may be poked through in defiance. The smell hits my nose with the force of a little nipper mouse trap, and with the ferocity of an oven left full on with a rancid chicken left inside it. If you are in any doubt about what this smells like I would advise you to live dangerously, take risks and, just once, try it! I make a mental note to clean out my cooker more often. I instinctively move backwards and hold my breath. In the same instance the occupant comes to the door. I explain as best I can why I have called. It is hard though, to speak without opening your mouth and hold your nose as well as almost being sick. Anyway I console myself that within a few minutes my nose will no longer be able to smell having been overcome by odour fatigue. This knowledge has been acquired by an interesting experiment at the fair town of Accy not a million miles from here. More of that in another story.

The gentleman beckons me in. I noted the multi coloured twine around his own trouser bottoms. It was of course tied in a neat bow. The small hallway had stacks of newspapers lining the wall to such an extent that the effect of walking down the hallway was akin to walking in another passage. I looked upward and saw the staircase lined with milk bottles, the contents of which I could only guess, and even with my acute powers of observation I deducted that it wasn't milk. The next room was entered, and if not for the door frame, it would have been impossible to know that we had changed rooms. The room was completely filled with rubbish of all descriptions. The only way to reach the kitchen was by a passageway that was literally a person's width. The rubbish was floor to ceiling. It was not possible to see what lay beyond the wall. In one corner, long before the invention of pyramid tea bags, was a small pile of used tea bags forming a perfect pyramid. Miraculously there was a small space for a table and chair with a

BAZ.

place setting consisting of a knife and fork on a newspaper. Well I thought at least he is being friendly to the environment and recycling his newspapers. By my reckoning he will have enough table cloths to last into the next millennium!

The kitchen consisted of empty tins in varying states of decay, in some cases the pile of tins nearly reaching the ceiling. The plates and cups in the sink almost provided a rival mountain. I dare not look down as my feet stuck to what remained of the carpet. Given the current popular television passion for decorating other peoples houses I wonder if a programme could be evolved around art deco garbage or tastefully decorating your neighbour's room with piles of old newspapers, *The Times:* for up and coming people and *The Guardian* for Liberals.

This was clearly a person not able to look after himself and in need of some care and attention.

"What do you do?" I asked him.

"Oh sonny I work over yon."

"Where's that?" I reply.

"Over yon butcher." he replied…

Oh dear. There is not a lot that can be done legally to stop him working there but we can get the house cleaned up.

I left the house to call for reinforcements. This was clearly a job that will involve a court order to get the house cleaned. A straight forward job? Well yes, but there was more fun and games to be had.

The house was visited by other members of staff and photographs were taken in order to apply for a warrant to enter the house and remove the rubbish.

Come the day of the court hearing the middle class magistrates were clearly shocked by the photographs. This sort of thing did not happen in suburbia. Their eyes lifted to the old man in the dock of the court.

"Have you anything to say my good man?" The chairman said.

"Well yes," our subject said his fingers nervously clutching his flat cap which was so greasy it looked like it would have a flash point lower than the local chip 'ole. "You've missed the best bits like where I climb over the rubbish to get into my bed and…" the magistrate silenced him before he could say any more and the court became in danger of total collapse from laughter. That is reserved for when we are watching "Home and Away" and are supposed to be considering our verdicts most seriously.

The day arrived to clean out the house. A council wagon accompanied by several workmen of course wearing the obligatory day glow colours. Word soon filtered back that as fast as the men removed the items our friend was taking it back out of the lorry and returning it to his house. What was to be done? It was more than the workmen's job was worth to stop him. So, by the end of the day the wagon was only half full. What was even more amazing was the emergence from the house of a motorbike and a piano. Some wag said that the motorbike was pre-war – perhaps it belonged to the same era as the telephone at Clogg Heads. Perhaps it was Renies from the days of her youth. Was there a secret liaison between Renie and the inhabitant of the house?

Eventually all was cleaned and our problem solved with the social services keeping a watchful eye on our subject.

All was quiet until one day when it was noted by a passing inspector that our friend who was renting a house from the council had no front bedroom window. When asked – and this is the absolute truth as may be verified by some extremely old inspectors he replied… "I have loaned it to a friend."

You can't have much greater friendship than that!

SEVEN

Bomb Making

ENVIRONMENTAL HEALTH OFFICERS are blessed with tremendous powers of information. Office staff have answered questions on local shop opening hours, train and bus times, the weather, lost dogs and the state of the economy.

One aspect that we have yet to answer is the way drains run. It is not until, like a creature from the black lagoon, when they gurgle up our sinks and toilets that we panic and reach for the yellow pages containing details of Mr Cost You A Fortune and "I don't know when I can get there," or "I'll be there this afternoon." Which translated means maybe next week when you have waited in and I arrived just as you had to pop out.

Very often there are no plans and the technology of drain seeking has yet to come along. I must add though that divining rods had been used to good effect. I always had sceptical thoughts on this until I saw our student in action. He used two metal bars – which we used to lift small manholes – held in front of himself at right angles to his body and held at waist height. When he passed over some water source they really did swing dramatically together. Of course, in the future we may well be genetically cloned to undertake this function.

In fact on one occasion the entire office thought that this had occurred when a partially sighted lady had rung the department saying that if a middle aged woman wearing a blue anorak and glasses had called to see her about a complaint she had made. This had caused particular consternation and had even caused our Grundy to put aside his treasured copy of the *Farmers Guardian*, the contents of which had been the subject of further heated debate in the office. Animal feed prices had risen again and the end of the world was nigh if his sheep could not be fed. There was some debate as to if Grundy looked like the sheep or they him such was the degree of empathy with their plight.

We all looked at each other, trying to rack our brains as to who the lady might be. Had we got a genetically cloned inspector before it had became fashionable to utter the word GM? There was a silence followed by a slow awakening, you could almost hear it coming... yes... we know... oh... yes you have guessed it... need I say more. I had recently purchased a blue anorak and I have a light voice. It had become common knowledge that we had two inspectors by the name of Lewis, one of a masculine derivative within the confines of the office and the other who "Superman" like changed into Mrs Lewis the instant he set forth from the office portals. She had obviously got the female version.

Before the use of mobile TV's to check drains coloured dye was used – no wonder the rats are looking so well groomed these days. These dyes came in different colours such as green, red, yellow and blue and were very expensive to buy. There were also several ways in which they could be used.

The first and very technical aspect was to make what we called a colour bomb. This consisted of a piece of tissue paper with several paper clips inside to give it some weight and add the dye to be used. I can hear you the reader asking, what on earth do you want to make a colour bomb for? Well you see, very often pipes, in particular eaves guttering are not easy to reach without the use of a ladder, which the local authority are unable to buy for want of the ready cash. They are also unable to hire the tower wagon as that also costs too much. This all sounds completely implausible but true.

The only available ladder had been climbed by myself several days ago to fix a microphone to the roof beams of the joinery department to measure the noise generated from the wood working machinery. When I climbed the ladder it bowed alarmingly, I had got into a position like the grand old Duke of York where I was neither half way up or down. After extracting myself I was told the ladder had been condemned and needed throwing in t'cut – canal – to swell the joints which makes the ladder more stable.

The manufacture of the bomb is an extremely technical matter for you must follow the instruction manual which was formulated by a very high profile government committee. It refers to such technical aspects as the strength of the wind, the quality of tissue and the weight of the paper clips. Too many paper clips wasted and the clerical staff get excited and the treasurers start to get quite hot under their starched collars. The main function of the prototype bomb is to be used to reach a length of guttering that may be running into a drain which is leaking.

The technique is to lob the bomb following a pre set trajectory into the gutter and then wait for the colour to seep out into the water to help to find

the fault. Easy you say but the lob takes many years of practice under the careful eyes of a senior. The user must also be a meteorologist as a detailed knowledge is required of precipitation levels – too much rain and the dye is washed out, too little and not enough dye is used. Also the strength of the wind may affect the trajectory of the lob. Note the use of the word "lob" and not "throw." This has been carefully thought out as a lob is much more gentle than a throw which may be construed by the inhabitants of the neighbourhood as a threatening gesture and summon the constabulary.

A further danger arises when the bomb is incorrectly lobbed. It strikes the roof and breaks, not only colouring the roof but there is a strong possibility that you may shroud the entire neighbourhood in a fine green colour – not to be recommended. The other drastic step is to have the bomb land on the house window sill and try to dislodge it with a powerful hose pipe as did one inspector only to find that the window was open and the occupant who was in bed received a good soaking.

There are of course other technical methods for using dyes. One is to pour the colour straight from the jar into the drain to be tested. This has the effect for the unwary that the wind usually changes at the last minute and colours the ever so immaculate inspector with his or her white shirt with fine colouring of whatever colour is being used. Great for the self confidence.

The final method used by the professional is to place the dye into an old jar whilst the kettle is switched on for a nice brew and fill the container with water which would mix with the dye and form a wonderful easy to use mixture which can be poured down whatever aperture is causing or suspected to be causing a problem. Feeling very professional I carried out this modus operandi filling a bath with water and placing my dye to allow a really good test to be undertaken. Being very house proud I cleaned the bath out and retired to the office to await the results of my highly technical investigation.

I waited for half an hour enjoying the tranquil atmosphere of the office. The silence was only broken by the occasional snore of one of our more colonial inspectors Charles as he rocked in his chair with his trilby slanted over his eyes – was he mistaking neon light for sunlight? He was the last person I can remember who used to raise his hat when greeting people. He was the last of the generation with impeccable manners. As the sun set he would often tell us tales of the far east when your chi or tea was bought by chi wallahs and there was none of this tea bag stuff and new fangled freeze dried coffee. Redrafting these stories I come to think that the characters are disappearing. Nowadays a manager will talk of best value and performance related work, and their language is as dull as they are.

Suddenly the tropical calm was shattered by the ringing of the telephone. I sprang to my feet. Was the call another result for my brilliant skill at solving the drainage problems of Trafalgar.

Wearily Grundy put the 'phone down, rubbed the top of his head as he usually did when either livestock prices had slumped or yours truly and made another disaster. He looked at me and exclaimed, "When you cleaned the bath down did you rinse out the Sponge?" I spluttered something about being careful. "Well" he said, "The lady had a bath and thought she had a tropical disease when she used the sponge, didn't you rinse the bloody thing out?"

Now some systems of drainage go directly into the streams and rivers as they take roof water which is essentially rainwater and therefore has no need to go to the sewage works. In this particular case our drain in question was of course wrongly connected but we were unaware of it at the time. The drain was repaired and we thought nothing more about it.

Several days passed and we reflected on how well we had done for contributing to the welfare of the health of the public. I put the kettle on for a well earned brew. All was bliss as the kettle hummed, tea cups chinked and the electronic clock – ah times have moved on – ticked. I am unable to confirm if it ticked by AC or DC. The radio was switched on to hear of the latest cricket scores. Occasionally we glanced up to see if Grundy was still alive and well despite the state of British farming. He was deeply involved in a conversation with some high sounding official. From the state of his voice sounded as though he was on the verge of calling out the national guard. He had received reports of some red mammalian footprints going through the local park and thought that the local slaughter house had been a bit over zealous and had slaughtered the local ducks. Grundy spoke with a soothing voice that the slaughterhouse was not killing ducks – not since some had inadvertently gained access over the Christmas period. Yes, he would look into the situation. Another joy for the hard pressed officer who was about to go home, his bicycle tyres nicely pumped up.

Soon the telephone was ablaze with calls from worried townsfolk who reported the local beck – stream – was running red and that countless murders had taken place.

The final straw was when the local angling club rang to protest that their choice angling water had mysteriously changed colour from the usual grey to red. Suddenly the penny dropped – and was picked up by Grundy! Of course. Our drain trace had gone into the wrong system and had found its way into the water course. The national guard was stood down. Grundy cycled off into the sunset and we reheated the tea – throwing the pinky red sediment into the sink.

As we sat back and reflected on our activities the reason dawned on me as to why my boiled egg appeared to have a rather pink tinge to it!

EIGHT

Mutant Frogs

IT WAS the usual morning post round as Top Cat, the boss, strode up and down the office floor handling out complaints of extreme risk to the general public from the general public. TC reluctantly gave me several complaints to deal with. His attention was drawn away as our usual late starter – Burglar B, so named because of his innocent involvement in the handling of some stolen spin dryers – sauntered in, toothbrush in his top pocket, sat down and immediately disappeared behind a pile of files. Burglar B was in held in high esteem as he once had called TC a silly bugger and got away with it.

I read the first complaint. The complainant had returned from holiday on the continent to find he was being being kept awake at night by the croaking of frogs allegedly camped in next door's garden. Now it was the wrong time of the year for frogs so it had sounded as though we had another batty complainant, not least because he was threatening to vault the fence and have the perpetrator frog marched away to some slimy cell. The last time we had a similarly batty complaint was when a Mrs Carrot had alleged that gold bars were being stolen from her outside toilet. It took the consid-erable skill of one of our more patient inspectors Jacko Wacko to persuade her that it was the bin men who were taking her rubbish and not the gold bars.

Jacko was the inspector who took milk samples from the milkmen on the district. Very often there would be a car chase as they tried to avoid him and he to catch them, but Jacko always got his man. Jacko was also a man of mystery. He drove a Russian car which appeared to have all the secrets of the Western world under a black tarpaulin covering the back of the vehicle.

The department sprang into action. Battle stations sounded, there was a whooping around the bridge as TC donned his oil skins and sounded down to the engine room to increase speed. The complainant's house was visited and the matter discussed. As in most complaints when you visit, the noise has either mysteriously stopped, was quieter before you arrived, or started again when you had left. On this occasion the noise was not apparent.

I remember on one occasion I visited a property where there was an alleged noise which I could not hear. The complainant rushed down to me before I drove off and proclaimed that you could hear the noise if I placed my ear against the bathroom wall. Some nuisance!

On this occasion, however, the complainant was clearly upset by the lack of noise. I explained that I could do very little unless I could hear the noise for myself. Perhaps the frog, tired of its game, had leapt into another garden to annoy someone else or else it had been knocked out by one of TC's depth charges!

I went on to my next complaint. I could hardly believe it. A takeaway meal which contained a piece of something looking like the leg of something amphibious, definitely not a chicken. Was this a wind up? Trying to keep a straight face, I promised that we would send of the piece to our laboratories and have the substance tested.

After the unsuccessful visit, action stations was stood down and we all hovered around feasting on hot drinking cocoa and corned beef sandwiches in the tradition of the best naval films. And in any case TC was the commander, the boss and we would do as we were told. I am not sure if TC wore a duffel coat.

As time went by, the complaint persisted and we decided to place a sound recorder on the site to see if it would pick up any of the noise. This is, in itself, a very interesting social phenomenon. Usually the more intelligent people manage to turn the thing off after having all the intricacies explained to them. Then there are the other sort, those who make a noise to "demonstrate" the noises they are complaining about. I remember on one occasion when you could hear quite clearly the two people discussing this and then producing the noise themselves. It is surely a strange world we live in.

So, the noise machine was taken and, as usual had to be delivered in the dead of night as the complainant was sure that the neighbours would spot it in daylight and cease making the noise. Come to think of it the neighbours can also see in the dark, so, either way it makes no difference. I explained the workings of the machine, how to press the button when the noise of the frogs can be heard. I then recorded my name and date in case the matter should end up before the beak in the magistrates court. I then retired to the office for more cocoa and corned beef sandwiches, plus more tales from the bridge of the destroyer.

Several days later a return visit was made to retrieve the machine. Back in the office the matter received much interest and the recording was placed before a hushed audience. There was a definite mechanical croaking sound which was loud. It was loud enough to wake our ex colonial inspector who, quietly dozing, thought himself back in the jungles of the far east. Even our local wildlife experts were somewhat confused. After examining several books on noise that frogs make, we were no nearer identifying which frogs could be causing the problem.

Suddenly our student, "The Judge" had an idea. He is thoroughly brilliant and looks as though he has been through a de-lux car wash in the morning, he is that smart and clean! He has a packed lunch assembled by his granny with such mathematical precision that it appears she has used a compass and protractor to work it all out. "Why not send the noise tape to the County laboratory. They might be able to distinguish the sound." He declared, crumbs flying from his mouth in a perfect parabolic arc. Not one landing on his pristine shirt. This was a brilliant idea. The boffins at county hall were wonderful people who could tell whether a cockroach had been cooked into a pie, identify some east european spider that had inadvertently crawled into a jar of west european jam and also identify an animal from a small bone fragment. So, the recording was dispatched and while we all awaited the results, normal activities resumed.

Several days later TC came into the office holding a piece of paper with a reply from the lab. He said that they were unable to place a species type to the noise, having profiled thousands of croaks of frogs from their world wide data base. The noise required a further test as it did sound somewhat mechanical. They were extremely excited at the prospects of possibly discovering a new species of frog. It was decided to undertake a visit at night to see if we could sort the matter out.

Upon arrival the complainant said all had been quiet except when his neighbour had gone out. Strange. Myself and "The Judge" venture out, groping our way down the garden not using torches for fear that we would give ourselves away either to the neighbour or the frogs. It felt very strange. There was an absolute silence this being a relatively rural area. Suddenly right behind us came a croak. A very definite croak. Such was my surprise that I jumped and in so doing, startled my companion who inadvertently slipped, getting a shoe full of water from the very slimy reptilian pond

"That was it did you hear it?" I asked? All was again silent save the sound of splashing water as my colleague drained pond water from his official safety boots and threw a piece of slimy weed in my direction. As we moved further down the garden there it was again. A definite croak but not like any frog I knew. I felt the hairs on the back of my neck rise. Being prone to having a somewhat vivid imagination I thought it could be the "Toad of the Baskervilles." Our ancient torch beam cut through the mist. Nothing. As we stood together the moonlight, which had been obscured by damp clouds of a Lancashire night emerged and illuminated the very pond that the poor old Judge had fallen into. He was also worried that his grandmother would give him a right telling off. The repercussions may well affect the geometrical design of his "snap." Then we saw a reflection shimmering, which became an eye, a huge unwinking eye. At the same time, it appeared to give a harsh croak. I could have sworn the noise was moving towards us. Without further ado we ran for it, leaving our torch to the mercy of the mutant frog which I was convinced was about to leap upon us and devour us with one fell swoop of its elastic tongue.

We reached the car. "The Judge" frantically turned the ignition. Nothing. I wasn't surprised. The car was as old as the ark and had more replacement parts than a stunt artist. He cursed, and loosened his tie. I don't know who was more startled myself or the car, for it burst into life, or should I say some semblance of life, and crawled away.

Back in the office the following day there was an air of suppressed mirth. Even TC seemed happy with himself. Something was strange. Grundy did not have the *Farmers Guardian* in front of him but a trade magazine, something to do with security I recall. He smirked, and handed me a copy. Something was very wrong. Either livestock prices had increased or he had arranged a transfer for me. I could have died. There, in bold headlines screamed "Security Toad Pain" says resident… I read on. A local neighbour had won a nuisance order from the local magistrates against her next door neighbour for causing a nuisance by the sound of audible intruder alarm frogs. Evidently the frogs are placed in the garden and will croak at the sound of any intruder. In this particular case, the frogs had been set to a very sensitive level and also a high decibel croak had picked up movement several houses away, causing a a disjointed symphony of croaks.

"So that's your problem," Grundy said, "a mutant audible intruder frog. You had better ring up the lab and explain. It makes a change for me to have to explain why we are sending samples of pigeon droppings. By the way there is someone downstairs with a complaint of a mouse dropping in a toad in the hole." He resumed his normal "end of the world is nigh" posture. I went downstairs.

"Ah Madame Lewis" – I think he was short sighted as well – "J'ai une rãclamation. Je manager le crapaud dans le trou aviec frits…"

"Oui, je rãpondre, entres dans et s'asseoir."

Translation, "I am eating the toad in the hole, with chips…"

"Yes," I reply, "please enter the room and sit down."

From above the staircase I could hear muted laughter. There is something not quite right about our Complainant. I wondered if it was the string of plastic onions around his neck or the five speed racer he has left around the corner which belonged to some fitness fanatic? I shut the door and got my notebook out.

Faintly from the floor above I can hear the sound of a destroyer siren, the sound of engine bells and a lot of nautical laughter.

NINE

Long Drop

THINK OF HANGING, a fall from the cliffs... no, I am talking about what would be described nowadays as a very environmentally friendly system of waste disposal, that is if you do not have a sense of smell and don't mind the rats armed with grappling hooks nipping your bottom when you sit on the contraption.

The subject is the infamous long drop toilet. The one which you hear old people talk about with fear. When they were small children they were scared of falling down the thing. I think on several occasions they did and were rescued, safe but a little smelly.

The long drop or waste water closet was a brilliant invention by our Victorian cousins. It consisted of a wooden toilet seat, mounted on what appeared to be as an upturned pipe a couple of feet in diameter, or should I say about half a metre. The pipe went down into the ground under the yard and into the back street, where it joined up with the public sewer which took all the waste from the remaining houses on the street. From there it ran to the sewage treatment works. Before this invention all the waste was kept in an area at the back. It is still possible to see some of the metal gates which were used to empty the contents. If not the gates it is very clear to see the opening in the brickwork of the outbuildings of terraced houses in Lancashire. This waste was collected at night by people called, "Night Soil Collectors," who took the waste to the local tip.

These toilets did not flush as there was no water. Water for flushing came with aplomb from the waste pipe of the kitchen sink – there were very few bathrooms. A further example of this brilliance was that obviously the waste from a sink was not a very powerful flush so the idea was to collect the water in a container which when full tipped automatically into the shaft of the long drop and flushed the waste away. A brilliant method of utilizing the waste water to good effect and not, as we do today, use treated water.

Treated water is used today because if waste water were used there would be a considerable danger of the two systems being contaminated. There is also the problem of something called back syphonage in which suction can be caused, sucking clean water into dirty and vice versa.

Whilst the system was a good idea it was fraught with problems. For some reason people only reported that the things were blocked up when they quite literally could not sit on the toilet seat. This led to a lot of dislike by the men employed by the council who undertook the unblocking of such toilets. I can verify this happening as I was around – just – when these objects of art were in use. The other great problem was that if an unsuspecting person threw a cigarette down one of them because there was a direct link to the sewer and the large amount of methane gas, there was a very considerable risk of an explosion. I remember one lecturer at Salford College in Manchester to whom this had happened. The whole surface of a driveway had been lifted and required re-laying. The lecturer was called Rodney Sheep and was in many ways totally eccentric. Perhaps he went into teaching before he could do any more damage. What Rodney had done was to test some faulty drains with what we call in the trade smoke rockets. These devices are rather like a firework in that they give off large amounts of black smoke. Naturally when used underground will emerge on the surface showing where the fault is. So what Rodney did was correct except in lighting the blue touch paper. The fuse ignited the methane. No doubt many generations of student environmental health officers will have heard this story. But then our Rodney was always the perfect gentleman always referring to his students as gentle folks as he twirled his hair and thought up his next story. In many ways Rodney was the last of a dying breed of inspectors with a story to tell and a laugh against himself which appeared to suffer from the effects of genetic manipulation as once started it would carry on and on and effect all of us.

It was not until some twenty years later that I came to appreciate the skill in the design of these toilets since the house I had purchased had in fact a waste water closet. The water closet was shared with the person occupying the front part of the house. I understand that one of the occupiers of my house had died in that very apartment. Several years ago the front part of my house was occupied by a builder who very often had a partiality for alcoholic beverages. I would often only glimpse him being drawn into his open darkened front door by the arm of some attractive young lady. Today was different. He had come to demand that he wished to use his toilet and where was it? Thankfully I managed to get rid of him, but I often wonder

BAZ.

if he had a case in law. All went very quiet on that front when he got up one night and forgot that he had removed the staircase. The fall was heavy but cushioned by Mr Guinness.

When removing the container for the liquid we experimented how the tippler mechanism worked by filling it with water. The design was brilliant, the water came very nearly to the top before the counter balance came into effect and the whole thing tipped and disgorged its contents. The mechanism was extremely fine, it worked time after time and the water never overflowed. By some strange coincidence a friend at work had a friend at Bristol University who was very interested in the whole tippler design to use as a teaching aid for his students. After agreeing a suitable price for the mechanism the whole thing was removed and put on display. I'm not sure if it still is.

So back to the days when they were in use. For the annual health report it was the job of the luckless student to go out and see if they could find out how many of these things were still in existence. Can you imagine going round all the back yards being young and naive as I was. If it wasn't for the dogs and rubbish it was the occasional person who was still in occupation of the thing and actually engaged in testing it when I called. This obviously didn't go down too well, especially if you had just climbed over the yard gate. The Local Authority gave grants to get rid of these things and replace them with the more traditional flushing toilet – still outside. The great difficulty with the conversion of these toilets is actually digging down through the heavy clay soil to reach the main sewer to ensure a proper drainage connection. Otherwise we would have our old friends back again. Rats, that is.

It was whilst I was checking on the work to one of these toilets that one of the workman paused on his shovel, looked at a young girl, pushed back his cap and remarked, "Eh I'd rather have a good steak Nowadays!" As we all paused deep in thought as you do when looking down a hole in the ground, a sound of rumbling caught our ears. Was it Lean shovels stomach or mine? Or worse still, could it be a hungry rat sharpening it's knife and fork for a tasty morsel of someone's toe or finger or even of a juicy bit of bottom? We anxiously looked around.

In the distance was a man in a wheel chair, his bright socks gleaming in the murky Lancashire weather. He was coming down the hill fairly fast, free wheeling, one hand held on to his cap, the other clutching onto his stick whilst also trying valiantly to guide the whole speedy contraption which appeared to be gathering speed. Running behind the wheelchair was an exhausted whippet quite clearly in need of some form of canine resuscitation before he went to meet the great bone maker in the sky. As the wheelchair bumped along the cobbles, eyes intent on what had been passed up for a good steak he called out, "beats walking!" As he flashed past I got a glimpse of those socks, something about the Boom Town Rats before he disappeared around a corner with a squeal of tyres, or was it another type of squeal?

What happened? Well, like a lot of things in life, it is more interesting to imagine the events that took place behind that secret corner in darkest Lancashire, or then it might be the subject off another "tail!"

So now 99.9% of these toilets have been removed and replaced with the modern flush toilet. We now no longer have to worry about Mr Rat. Children can sleep easy in their beds not having to worry about being lost down the pipe which with their imaginations probably went all the way to the moon.

The capacity for inspectors to blow up drains is still with us and in the dark recesses of some department you will still find apparatus made of brass and are fine examples of Victorian engineering. Perhaps one, the machine, not the inspector, might crop up on some antiques road show and we will all be staggered by how much it is worth.

Beware though, dear reader, for Mr Rat is never far away. He no longer has to dwell at the bottom of toilet shafts. No sir, he has never been better looked after. In some of the larger cities, our city slicker rat can dine out with his chums changing his cuisine each night dining at a la carte bins, skips and the leftovers on the street.

Rumours of the frenetic rise in keep fit gyms to keep their weight down has yet to be proved!

TEN

Matter of a Meaty Nature

PART OF THIS short story has been inspired a lady of the environmental health profession who campaigns with a quiet authority about members of the meat trade who feed you diseased meat. She speaks with a gentle passion at a venue which during the day fills with eager members of a giant corporation who chant with apian monotony the name of their wonderful company. She believes that you and I should know about this scam and put pressure on government to rectify. She represents a company whose motto is "Amicus humani generis." Translation, "For the common good." This company has no shares, and doesn't sound any good when chanted.

This, dear reader is nothing new. After reading this short story you may wish to read "The Jungle" by Upton Sinclair.* A story which documented the brutal condition of the Chicago stockyards at the turn of the century and highlighted the social conditions of the immigrants who worked there. Instead of raising an awareness of the social conditions, which the author intended, the book led to an almost immediate reform in pure-food legislation in The United States of America.

In my early days as a student I remember three small abattoirs in Witch Country, one each in Trafalgar, Higher Than Thou and Clogg Hall. Our job then was to inspect the meat and ensure that the diseased meat was prevented from reaching the food shops.

At the time of writing and updating these stories the issue of unfit meat has again reached prominence. Chicken meat which has been condemned and destined for pet food has been diverted back into the food chain by unscrupulous persons. Local authority Environmental Health Officers with the police have been very closely involved in tracking these widespread movements of unfit meat across the country and have seized vast amount of it. Some of this meat has ended up with some reputable suppliers who have bought it on the understanding that it was of a good quality. When the food was declared unfit to eat, the suppliers fought long and hard to prevent it from being withdrawn from sale. These portions were often at the cheaper end of the market and sold to people who could not afford to be particular about what they ate.

There are some salient points here. The cost of recent operations has meant that in future the police may not be able to allocate as much expenditure to this field of activity which may not be as sexy as Al Qa'ida, and also local authority funds are trimmed like the proverbial meat that has has been placed before you as lip smacking juicy chicken instead of the effluent covered flesh that is carefully washed before it reaches your good self. Ah, you may well say, "I will buy from the continent." Well dear reader I have it on authority from a member of the meat fraternity who has revealed that the problem in the UK was minor compared to what was going on in Europe.

It is at this point that "The Jungle" and our so called modern world combine and the wheel goes full circle for we are again eating what should be discarded. Perhaps someone will come along and write a book on what is happening to our chicken and meat today. Any way, I digress back to my story.

With our office being located in Clogg Head myself and Grundy or even "The Curate" would walk up the High Street to the local butchers. The small abattoir was located at the rear of the shop. It was always a constant source of amazement to myself how many these people my mentors knew. It seemed to take an age to reach our destination because they stopped to talk to so many people. I think this was one of the advantages of a small town council. One day we sat down together and reckoned that between us all there weren't many folk we didn't know.

Meat inspection in these small places was awful for it was often very cold and the meat numbed your fingers. A knife had to be used to cut into the meat and offal and one of the dangers was that because you couldn't feel your fingers you were in danger of cutting them. I have a weak left arm and had to be careful as my arm would tend to fall and cause my knife to slip. Very often these small places would just kill a few cattle and sheep. There was always one thing about the cold, the brew offered by the butcher at the end was very welcome.

Down in sunny Trafalgar the abattoir was run by a wonderful character named John Reed. John is dead now but I have great memories of him always offering to sharpen my knife and offering me some coffee from his flask. John was troubled by a runny nose due to the cold and from time to

time would wipe his nose on his sleeve as he spoke to you. The most hilarious time at John's place was during the time of Ramadan when the Asians killed sheep and ewes. The poor animal had to be killed facing East. At these times a great deal of humour and tolerance was called for as the owners of a particular animal would like to see it being killed and so at times we would have numerous white robed individuals wearing sandals hopping between animals. It was no use getting officious as often they would either feign that they did not understand or smiled and carried on as usual. Strange, sounds like a trait we can all use when we need to.

One aspect of the ewes was that by their nature they were poor animals and it was often borderline as to if they were fit to eat. The great problem was that the Asian people preferred the meat that way.

After my free transfer to Accy I worked in a rather larger abattoir which was extremely busy and there was often conflict between the workers and owners against the inspectors. I understand that this situation is much worse now with inspectors feeling much more intimidated. The problem had not been helped by an inspector who had been working there who I think got extremely stressed and started to arrive late. This obviously caused problems and he had got into a situation where he had left the meat inspection stamp either with the owners, or where they knew to find it. They stamped up their own meat and there was no inspection made. All this went undetected until one of our senior inspectors made an early morning visit and the whole situation was uncovered. There was a lot of aggravation and it was very hard to re-impose discipline. I am unsure what happened to the inspector, but it was a good example of a person who quite clearly had been unable to cope and instead of going for help had got deeper and deeper into trouble until as Macbeth would say,

"I am in blood Stepped so far, that, should I wade no more,
Returning were as tedious as go o'er."
Macbeth Act III, Scene IV.

I think there is a moral for all of us here, for how often do we carry on without thinking of how we can cope and then suddenly everything falls apart.

Work within an abattoir is hard and I think in many respects is enough to turn you vegetarian. One of the problems inspectors have is ensuring that the workers remember that it is food they are preparing and not just to regard it as a unit of production. Therefore, it was vital to ensure that knives used are kept clean and that the carcases left the abattoir in good condition. In all the abattoirs I have worked the people although tough and hard working are equally concerned with the well being of an animal. I have known occasions when if an animal had been ill treated the workers from the animal pens would come up to you and report the facts. In some cases this has lead to prosecutions.

To be working in one of these places was the closest I have ever come to working on a production line. I have never known such boredom as, due to the work involved, you are often inspecting one part of an animal for hours on end. You think that you have been really busy and you look at the clock and only fifteen minutes has passed. It is easy to understand how petty arguments develop and minor matters take on great importance. I can only say that I am glad I never had to work in that environment for any length of time. From a social perspective the work that most of the young people do is hard and physical and burns off surplus energy. Sometimes I think if there were more of those jobs about excess energy energy would be used up thus preventing other forms of aggression.

I always found that when working at Accy I would become almost passionate for a bacon sandwich from the canteen. I think it was the hard physical work, but it didn't turn me into a vegetarian.

Very often the unexpected happens when an animal escapes inside the building. This has happened on several occasions and is very dangerous. For one thing the abattoir is a very noisy place and you cannot hear clearly any warnings given. There could be a bull coming up from behind you, feeling frightened and cornered. Once in the abattoir a bull escaped and it was frightening to watch as it ran around clearly terrified, its legs slipping on the surface and its head hitting anything in sight. Some of the workers thought this a good excuse to show off their prowess and one of them bravely grabbed it by the neck and wrestled it to the ground in grand cow-boy style.

The most awful sound of animals dying is made by pigs. For some reason they squeal and make an awful noise, sheep obviously bleat and all crowd up in a corner trying to escape the person who is going to stun them. The squealing of pigs can be disturbing and this can sometimes be heard by residents. I remember on one occasion investigating a complaint from a nearby resident of pigs squealing from the local abattoir. I was on surveillance for this particular complaint. It was a sunny afternoon and I was reading a book, as I sat in the garden thinking, "this is the life," and munched some of the excellent home baking on offer from the complainant. Suddenly she came rushing into the garden shouting, "they are squealing!" and getting very emotional. I put my book down and listened very intently, yes I could hear them but only very faintly. I think that this goes some way to show how either my hearing wasn't very good or the person was very sensitive and very emotive about the whole issue.

After several sunny mornings and afternoons, even the sound recording equipment could only record the noise of passing traffic. Time was called and I ate my last piece of home baking.

The small abattoirs I worked in have now all closed due to changing economics and legislation. Some would argue with devastating effect with regard to outbreaks of foot and mouth disease throughout the country. Thankfully my time as an inspector came to an end with these closures and probably saved my fingers!

* The Jungle by Upton Sinclair. Publisher Penguin Classics.
  ISBN 0 14 03.90316.

ELEVEN

Rat Hunting with Jim and Rex

MANY YEARS AGO whilst still a nipper I trained as a Sanitary Inspector at bonny Clogg Heads upon the hill in Lancashire. We were based in the clinic directly opposite the old library and the war memorial. It was a very homely place. Upstairs was a clinic where the dentist could be heard regularly drilling his patients – the drill has always left me with abject horror after listening to a Radio Four programme – "Fear On Four" – about a man who had been cavorting with the dentist's wife. The dentist had found out and, that the man was his patient. When his opportunity came his patient quite unaware of what was to happen, was strapped in the chair and all you could hear as the programme ended was the sound of the drill. Your imagination did the rest. Radio is so good at that.

At the back of the office was a fully fitted kitchen where some of the staff prepared lunch. Often you would come into the office late in the morning to smell roast potatoes and stew. One member of staff, "Old Tom," used the kitchen to ferment some of his excellent wines. I seem to remember that even "The Curate' smiled when sipping the brew and myself being young and naive – I still am – wondered why the office walls moved after several glasses.

Every year the sewers of Clogg Heads were baited with rat poison – a job which is now undertaken by the Water Authorities. Jim, plus Rex accompanied by myself and another student would ride round in the van equipped with picks to open the manholes. We would put the a test bait into the chambers which were used for access to the sewers and also as a form of ventilation. The test bait gave us an indication of where the rats were as they would eat the bait. I doubt that that would work now as the rats are getting quite sophisticated in their eating habits. Wouldn't you if you had the choice of at least a dozen takeaways?

The chambers were made of cast iron and extremely heavy. We used the picks to lift them onto a form of hinge which enabled them to to be rocked. If you got the knack of rocking, the lid could be flipped back into position in one go. Today a special lifting device is used. This grew into a game and a competition to see who could get the most lids back in one. Often children would come out and ask us what was in the hole. Jim would usually reply, "goldfish." In all the time doing this work I never once saw a live rat.

The most fun we had was baiting the sewers on the Exchange Street side of town. We both sat in the back of the van and as it went up the hill our feet had to be raised to stop them being dragged along the road surface. Jim showed me how the cobbles were paced in an offset manner to enable horses to go up the hill without slipping. It was not uncommon to see vehicles in the beck at the bottom of the hill. I remember clearly one parcel van on all four wheels, as though it had got onto the wrong road standing in the flowing water.

In between sewer treatments we did our normal visits. One house we went to at the bottom of Knotts Lane was a local chip shop and had a very warm room heated by a coal fire. Jim sat, and like an expert, was discussing the merits of different bait and methods of catching rats and mice. The benefit of chocolate truffles compared to warfarin, a chemical agent which thins the blood of the rat. The conversation seemed to drift into the distance as chocolate, truffles and rats seemed to merge into the pleasant soothing sounds of the roaring fire and gentle Lancashire accents and I was fast asleep. The next thing I knew was our Jim prodding me and saying we must be off. It was the last and only time I have ever fallen asleep whilst on duty in a person's house. Memory isn't quite clear as to whether Rex was asleep as well. But then you would have heard his snoring!

One day at the office we received a call, via our outdated telephone system, that we were to visit a person who had a rat in their house and please would we go as soon as possible. The occupant of the house was frightened to death that the thing was going to consume them alive and that there may be more of the creatures around. Jim grunted, threw a biscuit at Rex and sipped the remainder of his tea from his cracked saucer. As the sound of slurping filled the office Rennie winced at his lack of refinement. She would at least have used a bone china saucer and slurped delicately as she perused her car manual. Departure would be post tea slurping, and biscuit munching when dog and human, excluding myself – I was not classified as human as I was still a student – were ready.

"It's in t'yard," said the occupant, Jim grunted. It was one thing to have to rapidly slurp tea, but to have to go around the back like a common tradesman rattled him no end. In the yard was a rat, my first sighting. It looked like a rat who had had a night out on the town or had gone several rounds with Mike Tyson, and had forgotten where it lived. In the blinking of an eye Jim walked up to it and with the best right foot I have seen, made contact with the rat and sent it hurtling into the yard wall complete with right boot. The rat hit the wall and like one of those comic strips slipped down it completely dead. The falling boot adding insult to injury as it fell onto the rats head. I was shocked by the sudden act of violence by an otherwise quiet and gentle person, but couldn't stop laughing as Jim hopped around whilst Rex was yelping in an excited manner unsure of whether to grab boot or rat. A quick sniff of offending boot sent him to the rat without undue delay.

Jim said to me afterwards, as he tied his laces, that if the rat had bitten him he could have got Weils disease or some other disease that rats carry. Weils disease is spread in water by the urine of the rat. It can affect sewer workers and inland water pursuit enthusiasts. We placed the dead rat in a black bag and made to go back into the house and back to the van.

"No you can't come back through t'house with that," said the occupant. So we had to walk all the way round the terrace before getting back. It was one of my first introductions to the thankfulness of the public.

Now of course Jim being diligent looked for further signs of rats and sure enough found the problem. A couple of doors up was an empty house where neighbours had heard scurrying movements. The property belonged to the council and had been empty for some time. Key in hand we went to inspect the property.

"Strange," Jim said. "The windows are all misted over. I wonder if there is anyone living there after all." A closer inspection revealed that at the bottom of the window there was no mist. This area of no mist was almost in a straight line from one end of the window pane to the other. Jim peered in for a closer look his peeked cap being bent as he put his forehead against the glass and tried to get a better view. "By heck." He muttered, and stood back and cleaned his glasses. "I'm sure I saw something move in there." He paused for a while scratching his head. "Appen it's Old Tom's wine." After several moment of reflection he looked again. "Bloody hell it's wick with rats, small white ones, everywhere." I looked myself and sure enough there were so many rats it was difficult to see a single one. They all seemed to

BAZ.

merge into a moving mass as they roamed over the furniture and fell from drawers and curtains. Then we saw the ones on the window sill. They were so thirsty that they had been licking the water from the condensation on the window. There was no other water for them to drink.

Fastening up our trousers with Grundy's unwearoutable baling twine we turned the key. Rex was so excited he could hardly contain himself. The door creaked open and a horde of small white rats rushed past our feet and disappeared down the street. Poor old Rex was so bewildered he was unable to chase any as he could not identify a single one. The smell, try magnifying it times a thousand. It nearly knocked us back out of the house. Everything was just a mass of movement. The sofa was full of nests and there were so many rats climbing over the mantelpiece that some were knocked off by the sheer volume. In several corners were the remains of other rats in varying states of decomposition. Not only was there not enough water, but a lack of food. They had turned to cannibalism.

Jim laid some bait, well in fact I seem to remember we retired and just poured the bait through the letter box and continued to do so until there was no signs of life.

Back at base camp over a much needed brew and a biscuit for Rex we found out that a couple had lived in the house and had been breeding pet rats. Last year they had left and it would appear that they left the rats to fend for themselves.

Worse was to follow, for the house had to be completely redecorated and all the plaster work replaced. The plaster had to be replaced because there were spaces behind it and the rats had formed nests there. Sure enough the poor builders had reported dropping ceilings, and as well as falling plaster dust, had been subjected to a shower of dead rats from within the cavities. Somewhere there is proof of all this as a video was taken of the proceedings.

Very often we came near to losing Jim. He periodically went into tremendous bouts of laughter over what I had done or our other inspector Stewart – my namesake – had been up to. Sometimes it was touch and go between Jim or Rex. Jim from being bent over double with laughter, or poor Rex mad with excitement as he skidded and slid down the lino covered office floor in pursuit of a biscuit thrown by Jim.

There was one occasion when myself and Stewart had been to an empty house. No big deal you may think. There had been fleas in the house, when it is empty the fleas lie dormant until the vibration of the floorboards when someone comes in wakes them up. They think, "ah a tasty morsel to suck," they don't complain about the quality of the blood. So of course when we returned we naturally started itching and scratching and saw these small white creatures jumping about on our bodies. Even reaching for a bar of soap to catch them was not enough – wet soap is one of the few ways of actually getting hold of a flea. This called for drastic measures. We had to get undressed and in full view of the entire office stand over some of Jim's delousing powder in the back garden whilst also holding our clothes over the fumes. I think the smoke or vapour or whatever it was would be banned in today's enlightened times but anyway we stood and danced around waving our clothes whilst poor Jim went into one of his fits and of course Rex got disinfected as well. The motto of this story is, one, ensure that the house has been fumigated and secondly wear the Grundy patented baling twine around your trouser bottoms; this prevents fleas jumping up your legs and provides Grundy with an income from which to buy his *Farmers Guardian*.

The last impression I remember of Jim was both funny and serious. For his duties he used a dusting powder which I seemed to recall killed cockroaches. One day the canister went off in his van and enveloped him in a white powder. I remember him coming into the office completely white. I also recall that whilst appearing funny it was surely not recommended to be covered in a form of poisonous dust.

Jim died long since. Looking back he taught me a lot and I am grateful for the experience I gained. The rat catcher has long disappeared into folk law and the name has now been upgraded to conform to some mission statement. Unfortunately the rats and mice are unable to read – yet, and continue to became larger "stakeholders" in the country. I wonder if they attend focus group meetings?

TWELVE

The Bacon Butty that Disappeared

MEMBERS OF THE public come into the department complaining of objects found in their food. These objects may be pieces of metal from machinery, slugs in lettuce or even cockroaches in loaves of bread. Sometimes, unfortunately the other half of what they have "eated" – as little children would say – is inside their stomach. Recently I visited an elderly couple who exclaimed that they had got some chicken pieces in their bread. On closer inspection the chicken turned out to be bread crumbs Things are never what they seem, rather like life. The odd piece of finger that is actually a piece of fruit, the currant that is a mouse dropping and the piece of vegetable reported as a fingernail especially if from a take-away. What wonderful imagination members of the public have.

One day a lady came into the Town Hall in high excitement, complaining that a bacon sandwich or butty as it is called locally which she had purchased tasted off, or as she said "bloody 'orrible." I was duly summoned. The reason for that was because I was a past master at detecting by the scientific method of digestion if a product was going to cause any ill effects. I had once eaten some mouldy cheese being kept in a fridge in Accy which was being saved to be sent to the laboratory for testing. When the cheese could not be found I had to own up. The story has stayed with me ever since. I spoke to the lady and told her that we would investigate the matter.

The said butty was transported back to the office in sterile conditions or at least wrapped in an old copy of the local newspaper – The Craven Almanac.

Back at the office it is the usual custom for everyone including the office cat to examine the said specimen. Before judgement can be passed it is necessary to infuse the mind with suitable herbal remedies. For good or evil we are moving towards more liberal times and the more traditional Yorkshire tea was being replaced by the more trendy staff with herbal teas. Making tea had now become a major test of memory as not only was it necessary to remember whose mug was who's, but which infusion each partook.

Now it may surprise you to learn that while some Environmental Health Officers are prone to preach over matters of hygiene, some are known not to observe such practices at home or in whatever domain they live. Some are so keen that they appear to live within the precincts of the department.

So, suitably refreshed we all gathered round the butty. It looked forlorn, sitting upon one of our slightly yellowed, cracked plates which still had the faintly embossed sign of some long forgotten council swallowed up in the name of progress and better value. The silence was only broken by the gentle purring of the office cat who so far had not been privatised. A small badge attached to his collar proclaimed, "Private cats good, public rats bad!"

"Don't seem much wrong with it said our senior "Mr Sanitiser," who was known to sterilize every surface he prepared his food on but didn't seem to concerned about the household cat helping him prepare it. "Smells good," said our student who owing to having to pay off his overdraft was in a dire food negative equity. New speak for starving. "Can I try a bit?" So he had a nibble and then a nibble became a mouthful until, what do you know the whole sandwich had gone and he was still here to tell the tale. "Crumbs, what are you going to do now?" asked Mr Righteous due to retire shortly. "You have no sample to send to the lab, and if we fail to achieve our target response and comply with the conditions of our mission statement as laid down in sub paragraph 2b with reference to sub clause 6…" He tailed off as Grundy our resident farmer told him to go and count the radio active sheep on the fell side. Evidently it had been on the Archers that the ministry for the opposition of farming was awarding a huge subsidy for the farmer with the most radio active sheep. The idea was to kill them, feed the meat to other animals to spread the radiation and thus keep the numbers down. They were of course denying this, and saying it was perfectly safe for sheep to eat sheep. To prove it, a Minister had even forced his pet sheep to eat another without any ill effects. All Grundy was concerned with was the money. Enough to keep him in Shag tobacco for the rest of his life.

A silence now fell upon the office; the only sounds were the clock ticking and our senior gently snoring. A gentle scurrying indicated that the cat was off to find something else for it's tea. The clock ticking reminded me to look into the retirement present for Mr. Righteous. "I know," said the student who had regained a more fitting pallor now that he had eaten, "I will ring

the complainant up and tell her that the sample has been organoliptically sampled and that everything is fine. It's a phrase I read in one of my text books."

"Oh go on then we have got nothing to lose." I said.

So our trusty student in his most official tongue rang up the lady and did exactly that and she was extremely happy with the action that we had taken.

So our story ends with everyone happy. It amazing what you can get away with if you have the confidence and barefaced cheek to brazen it out. So, beware! When someone ring you up with explanations using very long words, for they are not always what they would appear to sound like.

THIRTEEN

The Classic Comic Strip

BEFORE THE STORY unfolds let me explain that I was not employed by the clergy but by our Chief Environmental Health Inspector was and had always been known as "The Curate" for his very saintly persona and of his quaint way of raising his hat as he wished people good morning.

Many years after graduating – "The Curate" had given up hope that I would ever make a Sanitary Inspector – I was eventually given a free transfer to nearby Accy and Stanley. "Young Stewart," he said, "It is now the correct time for you to seek pastures new and spread your wings," He paused for a while, raising his head and holding his chin as though deep in thought, "And they do possess a modern telephone system." He gently smiled to himself and retired to his office calling over his shoulder, "Oh by the way Renie, bring me some Earl Grey with a touch of whiskey. I have due cause to celebrate." As he gently closed his office door I was sure I could hear a small cheer and a skip.

One of my fond memories of "The Curate" was visiting a bakers shop on a food hygiene inspection. As we entered the bakery he raised his hat greeting the owner. "The usual Mr C?" Said the proprietor, standing in front of his oven which even I could see could benefit from a blind date with some hot water. "Oh rather he said," and we sat down to a tray of tea and cakes. It could have been a Sunday afternoon in the parlour of some gracious house as we discussed the weather, the shortage of hot water and complemented him on his delicious buns "Delightful tea, good day." He smiled raising his hat as we left for our next inspection.

Reviewing these pages I must admit that a small piece of "The Curate" has stayed with me for I am offered cups of tea and coffee. In one case at a recent kebab factory in the great metropolis I had tea out of bone china cups complete with pizza and biscuits. Unprofessional behaviour I hear you cry. I think not, we often fail to communicate and in times of which I am writing with the world threatening to engulf itself we all should have the time to accept some acts of humanity.

Back to the story; I could almost imagine the merriment in the shop after our departure as shop proprietor and mice danced for joy in a circle around the oven proudly salvaged from "Our kids scrap yard."

I must confess, this may have been a carefully worked out strategy. There may well have followed in the post a stinging letter to the proprietor to increase the rent of the tenant mice and invest in some soap and hot water!

Back to my story and the description of that quaint telephone. Our First World War telephone exchange consisted of a finely polished box with a huge black bakerlite telephone mounted on a cradle. At the side were various little levers and a small handle for transferring calls to other parts of the building. I could never work it properly. Every time it rang and I answered it, I could hear faint gunfire in the crackling ether and the sound of men singing "It's A Long Way To Tipparary" and "Pack up Your Troubles In Your Old Kit Bag." accompanied by distant gunfire. This so disturbed me that I would cut "The Curate" off with the regular consistency of troops going over the top to battle.

This was one thing that raised the hackles of "The Curate" into the version of the devil incarnate. His lips would quiver and his delicate cup and saucer would rattle, rather nicely, of course, as it was bone china. "Renie," he would say, "please keep young Stewart away from the telephone." Renie, with her head in a car manual muttered her consent. She was too concerned at finding out what part of her car had fallen off today, and how to find out where it went and whether some kind man would put it back with some baling twine – we were in an agricultural area – and chewing gum. So, to Accy and Stanley. I was of course not going to work at the defunct football club but at the council which was made famous by the loss of so many of its young men during the First World War who made up the famous "Pals" battalions. The "Pals Battalions" were formed of friends, brothers and cousins from the town. They, of course, joined up for the Kings Shilling, to be back home for Christmas, with their chums and what jolly fun they would have and, "Their Country Needed Them." They died together causing a massive haemorrhage of a generation of young men from the town. Many of those streets still stand and it is easy to imagine them marching to the local railway station the cheers of the inhabitants bouncing off those grand but now slightly decaying public buildings.

Strange, I hear those voices calling out to me as again we declare our latest war will be short and quick. Those who die will only be remembered

by sons, daughters, brother, sisters, wives, husbands and lovers.

I remember when I was a student in Salford doing housing inspections there was a row of terraced houses with a small glass case mounted on the wall containing a list of those killed in the war. At Trafalgar and Clogg Heads College there was an art teacher who had lost a husband and had never remarried. There were those to whom marriage was not an option as there were no men left after the slaughter.

Back on a lighter note. Accy was some sixteen miles from my home in Barnoldswick but according to the locals was by heck a fair distance as tha couldn't go home for thee snap – lunch. I soon settled into the friendly town and office – how is it that hardship makes for most friendly people? – I started out on visits to ensure the shops were in tip top condition and safe for the residents to buy food from. On this particular morning I was to visit a local supermarket, nothing remarkable in that you might think but there was fun and more watery tricks, dear reader, than could be imagined.

Entering the meat department I remember pushing open the door into the preparation area when my feet were plunged into vast pools of water which seemed to be spreading at a very rapid rate. This seemed to be a rather strange sensation and one which I had not encountered before in my brief career as an Environmental Health Officer. I remember being in what was almost suspended animation – rather like when a car is going to hit you and seems to take ages before it does and everything goes in slow motion. Well, at last my eyes and senses gravitated upward from my feet, to see that I was surrounded by a group of burly men clad in white hats and coats – of course with the odd smattering of blood. What was most interesting though, was the expression on all their faces. It was of abject horror. Was I so frightening as an inspector? Was my hair net mixed with curlers – another trick once played on me by my oh so funny colleagues. Had they got something to hide? Could I, at last, find the cut up mouse or rat which went into the legendary pie?

After what seemed another eternity some-one spoke. "Oh gawd it weren't meant for thee, everyone seemed to be saying the same over and over again like a mantra but with varying degrees of astonishment. From out of the corner of my eye I could faintly glimpse a red bucket rolling around like a demented top on the floor surface. Bucket and water were in close proximity to each other. Could there be a connection, but how come a bucket and water were so close together when I had not kicked anything on my way in.

At last all was revealed… a member of staff had placed a bucket of water over the door top leading into the butchery department so that when it was pushed it fell – in true comic book style – onto the person entering, in this case me. It was in fact intended for one of the managers. Standing amidst the water I slowly counted to ten. Do I make a scene and look a fool or go elsewhere whilst I calmed down. I choose to disappear for a short time inspecting another part of the shop and return when I felt able to laugh at what, after all, was a very unusual occurrence and one that I don't think will happen again.

I returned t'office – another champion tale to tell.

FOURTEEN

The Miasma Theory as Applied to East Lancashire

"ALL SMELL IS DISEASE." Stated Edwin Chadwick, Sanitary reformer of the nineteenth century. Since time immemorial people have been affected by smells and claim that their health is affected. At one time it would have been the lack of sanitation as the following would suggest,

> "How the scientific asses preach
> about their poisonous gases,
> making havoc 'mongst the habititations
> of the lower classes!
>
> We, the Board of Health supposes
> ought to make sinks smell like roses;
> people now-a-days pretend to have
> such very dainty noses."
>
> *(Punch Magazine 1849.)*

In the mid nineteenth century medical opinion on the causes of disease was still forming, and there were differing ideas about the cause of people's illness. The two schools of thought were the miasmatists, who claimed that people were ill as a result of poisoned air, ie rubbish on the streets and an inadequate sewerage system and the contagionist's who believed that disease was spread by physical contact, whether from person to person or by eating infected food or water.

Both Edwin Chadwick and Florence Nightingale were miasmatists.

Nowadays there is a whole host of problems which have evolved due to our increasing technological age. Our own society has become so sterile that it is necessary for museums such as the Yorvik Centre in York and the

Thackeray Medical Museum in Leeds to artificially manufacture the smells of middens and toilets to remind us what it was really like

One such case was to affect a small town in East Lancashire and require the Men from the Ministry to try and sort out. Strange as it my seem the Men from the Ministry were in fact real life scientists who specialised in solving smells. They no doubt read the following letter printed in *The Times* of 5 July 1849 and started up their own business – I wonder if they received a Government grant?

> "We aint got no priviz, no dust bins, no drains, no water-splies, and no drain or suer in the hiole place... Preaye Sir com and see us, for we are livin like piggs, and it aint faire we should be so ill treted."

As an avid comic reader of the Beano, Dandy and Eagle comics. I have a vivid imagination and imagined these men to be wearing white coats with their hair standing on end and acting in a completely loopy manner, using very sophisticated machinery which steamed and bubbled. Can you imagine my surprise when these people turned up at Accy's long lost railway station looking completely bewildered. Clutching their equipment and wiping their round spectacles they asked the way to the council offices. Unfortunately they were misdirected and ended up at the nearby institution for people with mental difficulties. The situation was only solved when a member of staff rang our department to ask if we knew of a collection of white coated individuals with strange equipment, rubber tubing and drums marked "smell." They had also further distinguished themselves by jumping onto the railway line and measuring the famous curve of the viaduct using protractors and compasses After disentangling themselves they arrived and set to work setting up their very sophisticated equipment.

Back at the office news had seeped like the proverbial Lancashire rain through to us inspectors that the scientists had landed complete with equipment. Rumour had it that they had already visited the plant causing the problem and had bottled the smell to experiment with. Again my mind went into overdrive. How on earth can you capture a smell? It was almost like those stupid tins that you could buy containing London fog. Perhaps these people were really going to export Accy and Ozzy air to people down South. Perhaps they were frauds who came in the guise of scientists.

BAZ.

So, by and by we were requested to meet the scientists to help in their quest to solve the problems of the foul and malidiforous air of North East Lancashire. Clearly there had been no thoughts on the merits of exporting the stuff.

We entered the room and were confronted by a group of boffins. At first they seemed to be speaking a strange language which sounded like the square root of the smell equalling the pong divided by the equation of the central lowlands. In front of them stood a strange machine which had horizontal cones sticking out of it. We were supposed to sit on high stools – or buffets as they are called locally – with our noses in these cones and indicate by pressing a button if we could smell anything. The smell was contained in a plastic drum with – you will not believe this – a label marked "smell" on the side. Despite all the technical equipment around us the drums were mounted on old tea chests marked "Product Of China, This Way Up." Of course they were upside down A casual glance around revealed other drums marked "not so strong" and "what a wiff." The scientists seemed to be in great excitement as they watched us sitting at this contraption with our noses in the cones. The great problem was that we could not work due to the hilarity of the situation. The white coats grew annoyed and jumped up and down, their white hair becoming even more distorted. They kept taking off their glasses wiping them and muttering "how very important these tests were," and, "would we please mind ever so much if you don't mind, if we would settle down!"

We decided on a break and asked the boffins if they would like some tea of coffee. "Oh rather," they all seemed to say in unison, and then individually, mine's a tea with a specific gravity of 1.6, a temperature of 20 degrees Celsius or is that Fahrenheit, and oh, Faraday's must be stirred at a constant rate of six revolutions per minute in an anti clockwise direction. Suddenly they saw the bemused look on my face and said in rather embarrassed tones, mines a tea, milk no sugar and so on.

At last as true professionals we obeyed and the men got down with great glee to connecting one drum of smell to the agent which would stop the smell and so on. The interesting thing about these experiments was that certain people were excluded as they could not smell. Your nose will only smell something for a very short space of time before it will get used to it and no longer register. I was one of the "better smellers" and was kept on. This greatly relieved my boss as he knew that whilst sniffing there was a greatly reduced chance of myself getting into any more serious scrapes for the duration of the experiment. I think that he probably wished that the boffins would reduce me to a miasma and cart me off to their laboratory. I am afraid he was sorely disappointed.

And so the great experiment continued. As to whether the experiment was a success I can no longer remember, but I will always remember the mad scientists and the drums marked "smell" and "extra strong smell."

Poems from For The Common Good, 150 Years of Public Health. Chartered Institute of Environmental Health.

FIFTEEN

Events of an Unexpected Nature

I WILL START this narrative with a short outline of a story I read in a national newspaper about the survivor of a ferry disaster which in some ways applies to this story and makes you think about life.

"People become very philosophical." He said. "They thought they knew where they were going and what was going to happen to them, they thought they could plan the future. Then suddenly they receive this signal which tells them they have no control over life. It alters their values and direction, changes their emphasis on what is important."

A normal day. The clock ticked. The telephone rang. The call was from a person having problems with the heating of their rented home. They had received no joy from the landlord. Would we visit and offer advice. The house was located near the small hamlet of Trout Beck, Yorkshire. The weather was atrocious, wind and rain lashing down but we must go and carry out our duty. I had no need to fear the elements as I had my faithful student with me. We had nicknamed him "The Judge," after we had heard of a member of the judiciary with the similar name. If, there were any problems he was sure to have the up to date knowledge to solve them.

The hamlet of Trout Beck was so small that it had no street names or house numbers so we did expect some difficulty in finding it. As we drove up the dale "The Judge" told me of the latest mathematical formula that his grandma had come up with in order to squeeze more food into his lunch box. The reason this conversation had come about was because once I had remarked how well ordered it was and that it must have been packed with mathematical precision. I was only secretly jealous as my sandwiches were often thrown together like some picture by Picasso or other piece of modern art.

Reaching the hamlet we stopped the car and tried in vain to locate the house. At last we found the address or what appeared to be the property and knocked at the door. The door slowly opened and this rather elderly man appeared covered in soot. I could not believe it but his face was black and all you could see were the whites of his eyes. Rather stupidly I started to blurt out, "Is this the house…" before I realised it was and it took all my willpower to stop myself from laughing, the sight was so strange. "The Judge" was much more lucky, he was a little behind me and managed to hide behind a wall whilst he got over his fit of laughter. The problem is when you are not allowed to laugh the situation gets more acute and becomes even worse.

The man invited us in and on the other side of the room was his wife also covered in soot. Between them the fire billowed smoke uncontrollably and had covered everything, including the teapot from which we had been kindly offered a brew. I'm not sure whether it was the type of tea but it tasted a little on the sooty side. I was able to confirm a degree of soot on the cups as my lips had left a good "fingerprint" upon the rim. There was soot on the chairs, on the table and the dog was also covered. After talking to the people it became apparent that both were in need of some form of social help and contact was made with the social services. We also got in touch with the owners and arranged to have the chimney swept after which we heard no more of the sooty trio.

So, it was time to head back down the valley for a soot free brew. "The Judge" used a handkerchief ironed with surgical precision by his grandma to remove the soot from his mouth. He muttered about problems when he

would inevitably be asked some awkward questions about how the substance had got there. I replied that at least it wasn't lipstick as that may have given her heart palpitations and severely affected her sandwich packing ability.

The rain was now increasing in its ferocity and tumbling down from the high moors and fells around us forming a vast stretch of water across the road. We slowed down and surveyed the scene. Coming in the opposite direction was another vehicle which appeared to make it without too much difficulty. I decided to proceed and slowly drove forward. "The Judge" leant out of the window and pretended to measure the depth of the water with a plumbline, probably used to measure the vertical stacking of his sandwiches or the perpendicular crease of his trousers which were shortly to be severely tested. We slowly crept forward, my brother had once described the way I drove as in Braille.

At the time of this story I had also obtained my British pilots flying licence and had taken several people into the skies above Lancashire and Yorkshire and had brought them back to earth in one piece; well just about. These passengers who had risked life and limb had often remarked that I was safer to fly with than to drive. What usually happened was that I was so relieved to be back on the ground that I would make some elementary mistake whilst driving like failing to see a red traffic light!

Back to the story, in the opposite direction came another car, pushing a bow of water in front of it and going rather fast. The timing could not have been better, the bow wave from the car surged in front of us and right in the middle of this lake the engine stopped with a gentle bump. In the ensuring silence the water gurgled into the mat well and it was quite apparent that we were not going to move. "The Judge" as resourceful as ever rolled up his trousers and took of his shoes. He then got out of the car and pushed me to safety, his socks and shoes left in a neat pile on the passenger seat. Slowly, ever so slowly, we rolled out of the water and onto a piece of dry land.

As he climbed back into the car to put back on his socks and shoes I remarked about his trouser creases. "Oh not to worry they're everpress." He remarked as he tied up his gleaming shoes.

So, there we were beached miles from any where with a dead car. Luckily there was a nearby pub. We knew the landlord who assisted us to summon assistance from our extra mural lawn mower repairer who was an expert on engines.

"Reders the every ready" towed us, rather like Mr Toad, deflated and wet, back to the office. He confirmed the worst about my car. It was a diesel and had through the air intake which was a little low, sucked the water in to the engine. Diesel cars compress the fuel to produce a spark – unlike petrol which is ignited by a spark – the water refused to be compressed and instead bent all the piston rods. Lots of other things to do with cars which I didn't understand also got bent. All that I knew was that it was a very expensive job and the motto is when in a diesel car always be careful where there is deep water!

Later back at the office I reflected on the number of uses that a student can be put to. I made a mental note to perhaps write a short book on a hundred and one uses for a student environmental health officer.

So beware a routine day may be anything but!

SIXTEEN

Lintels and Spin Dryers

This story is dedicated to the memory of two Environmental Health officers John Bineham, who died of throat cancer and David Harrison retired due to ill health.

"SARACEN HERE." The voice grated like boots on gravel. His voice was enough to put you off wanting to continue with your telephone conversation. At some time in history he would probably have scared some granny to death wondering who she had been put through to. I often thought if the authorities had needed to use a photo fit voice on "Crime Stoppers," his would be the top notch because surely was the one to fit all criminals. No amount of smarmy canape courses had managed to rid "Saracen" of his appalling telephone manner. We were stuck with it.

At the time of redrafting this story I understand that voice recognition has been used by the authorities to prosecute individuals. There are arguments regarding the adequacy of this evidence but his voice would surely be an exception to the rule.

When "Saracen" wasn't on the telephone he would march around the office full of nervous energy. If he stood still, it was a national event! At last a word was said to him on the move as usual. I needed his help on a health and safety inspection. It was a bit bizarre really. There was a builders merchant in town where we were not very welcome. We were always receiving complaints of sand blowing from his yard and getting in to pensioners' false teeth. Or, having bonfires and ruining neighbours washing. The owner was a hard working bloke who disliked the local authority and had also termed himself "Lord Law Unto Myself." The title "Lord" had been purchased through some magazine like "Exchange A Peerage." None of which I had a problem with as long as he complied with the law and did not upset his neighbours.

The problem was that I had inspected the yard that morning and had seen several concrete building lintels standing on end. Any person having a degree of common sense would store them in a horizontal position. I had informed his Lordship that they were in danger of falling over. There was a problem with children who occasionally got into the yard when it was closed. We discussed that, although the children shouldn't be in the yard, it was a rather harsh punishment if one of them was crushed by a falling concrete lintel. Anyway I "requested" that he store them correctly and said I would come back later that day to check if the work had been carried out.

The time had come to re-inspect and I wanted "Saracen" to come with me to witness the problem. So, after several cigarettes, a long discussion about some good deal relating to cheap spin dryers with "Bonham" – another eccentric health officer who brushed his teeth for exactly two minutes and thirty seconds each day – and several circuits around the office, we finally got into Saracen's clapped out old car. As I dug my way in, I nearly lost an ear. "Back." He growled with a worse accent than when on the telephone. The dog, some huge Alsatian from outer Siberia appeared to cover its ears and retire into the depths of the back seat where it appeared to read some very old copies of "Radio World," which were scattered around, "Saracen" being interested in amateur radio. I realised how lucky I was not to have had an argument with those outsize teeth. So off we went in a car that looked like a giant mechanical porcupine with all its radio antennae sticking out of the roof.

We arrived at the builders yard and, of course, true to form the lintel was still there standing upright on its end. You could see it quite plainly swaying in the gentle breeze. "Saracen" decided that we would photograph the offending lintel and recommend a prosecution. Now the local authority we worked for were known to be a little behind the times and poor old "Saracen" had to set up his tripod, put a black cloth over his head and request yours truly to hold the magnesium flash gun. All very well but it was becoming increasingly difficult to obtain magnesium from our local chemist. We were also entitled to remove the offending object as evidence which we proceeded to do after informing his Lordship and giving him the necessary receipt. All this was carried out prior to the printing of ready made forms and much to my embarrassment the receipt was written on a page of "Saracen's" notebook which had been chewed and paw marked by "The Hound of the Baskervilles." As we struggled with the lintel poor old "Saracens" car nearly buckled under the weight. The dog, thinking that this was his day leapt upon the stone thinking it was giant bone. I'm not sure who came off worse, dog or lintel. The dog soon gave up trying to chew this new occupant and sulked back into the seat, a menacing look in his eye suggesting that he hadn't forgotten that trick played on him by his master and that he would in due course have his revenge!

Slowly we drove back to the office and got the lintel out to store it before presenting it to the magistrates court. Proudly both myself and "Saracen" posed before a camera with our new trophy. Wild concrete lintels as opposed to tigers! Whilst all this was going on I could see the dog looking on with an air of disbelief on its face.

Back in the office everyone admired our trophy and after a suitable interval "Saracen" asked "Bonham" about the good deal relating to the spin dryers.

"Well, eh it's like this," pause whilst he thought about the next line. "Bonham" was awful like this his voice over the 'phone was the exact opposite of "Saracen." In fact whereas "Saracen" could almost frighten you to death poor old "Bonhams" voice would lull you to sleep as I'm sure it did to a number of people or should I say clients now? He also had to spell his name out, every time he spoke to some-one. "Bonham," he would say, "that is B O N HA M." This got into such a habit that there were times in the office when we would all chant in unison as he spelt his name out. "Bonham" was always very particular about his name and he was also late for work, but he was always there well after close of play as Top Cat would say. Top Cat was the boss.

"Bonham," though a complete eccentric had an even more eccentric habit. It was fire engines. If he heard or saw a fire engine he would immediately follow it to wherever it was going even though he was at work. This degree of eccentricity rose to an even higher pitch when the Green Goddess fire engines were used during the Firemen's strike. Once seeing one going down Carr Road in Trafalgar we all thought he might be in danger of having a heart attack.

Redrafting this story I note that once again Green Goddess fire engines are again being considered in view of possible industrial action by firemen. History runs in circles.

I remember calling at his house once and discovered that everything in the fridge was wrapped and had it's exact position, enough to drive me mad. Anyway we got round to talking about the very cheap spin dryers that a friend of a friend knew and so "Saracen" along with half a dozen other people in the office had one.

After writing up evidence and seeing our very own "Perry Mason" famous TV lawyer we were bound for the Magistrates court with our pet lintel. The main problem was how to get it into court without firstly either rupturing ourselves or damaging the court furniture. So "Saracen," "Perry Mason" and myself formed an unusual trio in the public part of the court along with all the other hoi poloi there. Luckily we were allowed to take the pet lintel in slightly before and gently place it against some seat hoping that it would not develop legs of it own and move.

As we sat down there was a case going on about some poor person who had got caught without a TV licence. Before fining the person, the Magistrate asked the clerk of the court how much a licence was. Whilst this discussion was going on some wag whispered loud enough to be heard. "I bet he 'aint got one that's why he's asking." A stern look across the well of the court made the originator turn into a pillar of salt. Whilst not watching TV, the Magistrate was not idle and spent hours in front of the mirror practising his very own scornful look. This hobby though was getting a little expensive in that His Worship had to go to the the local D I Y store to buy another mirror, as they seemed to crack for no apparent reason. There was one silver lining, following Jack Hay's initiative on cracking down on crime, Magistrates who practised scornful looks would would be given a special European Community grant. A European Commission had worked out that the loss of revenue from replacing mirrors was in reverse proportion to the cutting of the cost of crime. I understand a fresh evaluation is to be discussed with reference to the Euro.

Our case was next. The defence solicitor pleaded guilty and in the process having bowed so far I thought he too had developed a bad back from carrying lintels. In mitigation, he spoke with a voice so sickly loquacious that it sounded as though his larynx had been lubricated with some sort of engine oil. It wasn't, though, a fast performance. He droned on, no doubt being paid by the amount of words used. Trafalgar was always a bit behind the times. To the gentle sound of the most heartfelt Jewish violin music – supplied by some job creation students from the local college – he offered the court a hard luck story, which the council was unable to challenge. His mitigation went something like this; The lintel was damaged, it had been savaged by a dog and was unusable to any self respecting builder, it had not fallen on anyone, the owners granny was ill, it was raining etc.

The defence was in danger of becoming worse than "Bonham." The Magistrate stifled a yawn, raised a hanky with the words, "I love the Boom Town Rats," wiped away a tear and retired to consider their verdict. As the door opened for them the gentle sounds of "Home and Away" from the TV drifted across the court.

Suddenly all was merriment. The defence and prosecution greeted each other like long lost enemies, the clerk to the court got his sandwich box out. The poor defendant stood alone in his dock like a child not invited into the party. The worrying point though was that the party could go on for twenty years or more before it was discovered that the poor defendant was innocent. "Never mind, what a shame." The clerk to the court would declare. "He had probably done something wrong down the line which we had not found out about."

The magistrates came back in with their verdict. Was the defendant to be told that he had to carry the lintel back to his yard on his back? No, nothing as dramatic. I don't remember the fine except to say that it wasn't such an amount that I will remember well into my pension years. I do know that the lintel felt twice as heavy in the carrying out as it did to the grand entrance.

One thing I do remember about that court appearance was seeing a man who had been charged with the murder of several middle aged ladies, I had obviously escaped (see earlier story). He was never found guilty as he committed suicide before the trial. I do remember him in the dock on remand. The strange thing about it was that he looked just like an ordinary person, like anyone's father, who had just got out of bed. There was nothing demonic about him just to outward appearance an ordinary guy. That was the frightening thing about the whole episode that I will remember.

Back at the office, events had overtaken us. It turned out that the spin dryers had fallen off the back of the lorry so to speak, and several officers were extremely worried. Technically they were in possession of stolen property. Sergeant "Sid Criminal" had been in to speak to Top Cat about the episode as the guy who had sold the driers on had given the names of those buying, perhaps to make things easy for himself. That night there were some worried people. "Bonham" had been one of those involved and naturally had become synonymous with the name "Burglar Bonham."

Poor old "Burglar" died of throat cancer several years later. Visiting him in the hospice at Ilkley was a salutary reminder of the side not many see of the effects of smoking. I will always remember "Burglar" saying to me that if he had one last wish in the world it would be to ban cigarettes. He had difficulty talking and swallowing. "Burglar" was taken care of extremely well by the people and there are times when you think what a good job the hospice movement does in allowing people to die restfully without pumping them full of unnecessary chemicals in order to prolong life for a little longer at the discomfort of the patient.

Like most things of a catastrophic nature situations always appear worse than they really are. We live through them and come out the wiser and in time laugh about it or make sure that we don't go down that path again. On this particular occasion the spin driers were recovered and returned to either the lorry driver or the owners. I think the participants lost their cash but I think all involved were extremely glad that it hadn't been far worse.

The episode mentioned will have been forgotten, except for those involved. But the name "Burglar Bonham" spelt B O N H A M will stay!

SEVENTEEN

Death: Always With Tea

IN TIMES OF war or civil emergency various councils of the United Kingdom are required to organise the burial of the dead. This duty often falls to the Environmental Health Department.

Even in non war situations people die and there is no one who will take the responsibility for their burial. Sometimes they have lived on their own and it may even be several weeks before they are missed. The body starts to smell or even degrade to such an extent that the fat liquifies and seeps through the floor. This may happen in a flat where there are occupants below.

On one occasion, neighbours alerted health officials to a smell coming from a nearby flat. Upon investigation, officers found a bath full of bones, fat and water plus the usual amount of flies. Naturally the cause of death needed to be ascertained – after all it could have been a murder. The expert in this case collected the fly larvae and sent it for analysis. It turned out that the fly larvae contained a high amount of barbiturates. It is probably a fair conclusion to say that flies are not in the habit of taking sleeping tablets. It was therefore decided that the person probably had taken an overdose of barbiturates.

The Local Authority must bury such persons and, if possible, reclaim any expenses possible from his or her estate. Invariably though, there is no estate. This is a function which is essential for public health, yet is not widely known about.

One such burial that I attended as the sole mourner and representative of the council had its funny side. The coffin was loaded onto a small hand cart which turned out to be slightly too wide for the church door. A great deal of undignified pushing and shoving eventually got our body through not without considerable loss to the paint work and chipped woodwork of the coffin. If that wasn't enough, there followed a great debate as to whether the church authorities had placed the coffin the regulation depth under-ground. Naturally, with the burial being a cheap job, it was presumed that some-one had skimped it to keep costs low. It turned out to be a misunderstanding; the grave digger had misunderstood the new fangled metres with good old feet and inches.

No doubt the body would be left to rest for as long as the local authority would allow before deciding that the plot was uneconomic to maintain. It could then sell the site to some entrepreneur as a theme park where you can experience death as a life style choice – "the death you want to live." Perhaps you could choose from some exclusive range of after death products which they are desperately selling in order to keep themselves solvent. An exciting, sustainable venture involving a partnership with the dead and living. A joined up approach to lateral thinking on two planes! I heard that the scheme had been silently shelved owing to the difficulty of consulting the dead person to review the quality of service provided.

Apart from the burial, the property of the deceased is often visited to see if there are any valuables left which may defray expenses incurred – what wonderful jargon. I have been to several such properties and often there is nothing. Bare cheap furniture, several pictures of friends and family smiling on some long forgotten outing. A bare mattress and a silence which is so profound it deafens you. This is our society. A life lived, and forgotten to be skipped and buried as cheaply as possible only noticed when it gives offence to the neighbours.

Sometimes a person may die with a pre-death request for his body to be shipped to his place of birth. I had experience of this myself once (not in a coffin). I was called to the undertakers to verify that the coffin itself was suitably sealed. The deceased was a Cypriot and it was necessary for the body to be enclosed in a metal coffin and the joint between the coffin lid and body of the coffin soldered, clearly an unusual job for a plumber.

Local Authorities have good working relationships with undertakers for they register deaths with the local authority and usually call in every week for this purpose. One particular undertaker was no exception, always jolly and with a tale to tell, usually about death to be accompanied by the obligatory cup of tea. I arrived and was told "to hang on" a few minutes. Sitting in the waiting room with plastic flowers and crucifix, my eyes drifted to the magazines at the side of the chair. "Undertaking Today" and "Practical Undertaker." Both with glossy covers featuring gleaming cars and shiny coffins and crematoria taken on sunlit days with, I noticed, no smoke coming from the chimney. I marvelled at the contents. One headline

"No, lad – I said bring me some solder!"

proclaimed, "Environmentally friendly" coffin will reduce pollution by using new wood glue. There were other articles on new improved furnaces and coffin fitments I never dreamt that such magazines could exist but they clearly do. I wondered if they have a page three coffin. Before I had to chance to look I was dragged back into reality by a summons.

I went down a series of gloomy rickety stairs, the sort the public don't see at an undertakers, and went into a small room. There before me was a metal coffin with a group of people sat around it as though it was a table. Stood on it was a teapot gently steaming, mugs, sugar and milk – in a bottle – plus, of course, the plumbers soldering gear. Neatly folded, as if to scrunch up would be an affront to the occupant of the coffin, were copies of the Sun and the Mirror newspapers. All sat with rapt attention, watching the master craftsman at work as he intricately blended solder and hot iron to fuse the silver liquid which would seal in our friend on his journey. Oh, and I nearly forgot, the caps placed on the lid in respect. I broke their concentration.

"Oh eh up, sit down lad, would thee like a brew, jobs nearly done, ah, he's well sealed in." The smell of fresh tea mingled with the solder fumes as we sat and discussed the state of the world. I never did see what was inside the coffin as the solder was well nigh nearly complete, but then if it contained drugs, we were all surely damned. If you couldn't trust the undertakers, who could you trust? I well remember the parting remark. "It'll take a tin opener to get him out at t'other end!"

I have found that such occasions always have their degree of humour which I think is an emotional response to what can be, and often is, a trying occupation.

I remember going early one morning to supervise the exhumation of a body which had been placed in the grave the wrong way round. His wife had heard about this and wished to have her husbands head at the headstone end. I was very touched by the manner in which the workmen undertook their work with the occasional remark about not letting "t'bugger fall out from bottom of coffin," as they raised him before turning the body round. It is also a rather quaint that such requests are taken very seriously and carried out in a very sincere manner.

With the fall in church attendances and the disuse of grave yards, in many cases churches have decided to sell of land and use it for building purposes. Before they can do so they have to ensure that there are no objections to the proposal. All bodies in the grave yard must be exhumed completely and all remains re-buried elsewhere. All work has also to be screened away from prying eyes.

One such site I visited was in the Midlands where the owners of a redundant church were intending to build on a graveyard last used in the nineteenth century. The graveyard contained hundreds of bodies and clearly could not be carried out by one man and his shovel. A contractor would be required.

I had an invitation to visit the site, not everyone's cup of tea. But then, if you do not take an interest in your work there is only yourself to blame for making it boring. Plus, there is the need to gather material for my stories.

The site consisted of two of what were the equivalent of metal containers, one for placing the dug up remains in and the other, the site office. The site foreman had made a very special effort for his visitors. On the table were green hand wipes used as place mats, and tea cups complete with saucers. Such gestures always stand out to me that here is a person who obviously takes a pride in his work. So we sat down to tea and he told us what the work entailed. It was of a very specialised nature and there were very few people able to do it and they were therefore kept very busy going all over the country. He was an expert on graveyards. I listened with rapt attention as he told us of sites from the plague in London to sites where bodies were buried standing up to save room.

After several cups we went up to the site which was surrounded by metal screening within which an excavator worked, with workmen removing the bones and pieces of wood from the site into black plastic bags. I understood that the headstones had all been smashed and buried in a deep hole. It seems a shame that such evidence is lost to historians and genealogists.

The workmen knew the depth of the graves so the digger removed the top layer of earth and went slowly as the grave level was reached. It was amazing seeing the graves exposed. In some cases the earth was just a different colour with the contents breaking down into a soil constituent when exposed to air. With others, bones were exposed which were then removed. I think the most poignant sight was seeing small perfectly preserved coffin lids being exposed which had belonged to children. The tops were taken and thrown into a skip along with other fragments of broken wood. The site was strange, a world within a world of metal screens, black earth and mud.

A friend was recently telling me of an excavation carried out in Sheffield where the site was required for the new Sheffield tramway. In this case, archeologists were used as the coffins were known to be lead lined and therefore possibly airtight. This would leave the contents untouched until they were exposed to the atmosphere. She was describing how perfectly preserved bodies were found complete with nightcaps and nightwear. An interesting insight into the attitude towards death in Victorian times.

One often hears of tales of skulls being kicked around these sites. I rather think the story is like that of Chinese or Asian restaurants where it is alleged that rats or cats go into the food. A rumour without substance. In my experience the people involved always act with a great deal of respect and such tales are very far removed from the truth.

As the age of the crematoria grows we may move on to different stories of workers heating kettles over the flames or even making toast, but then in these days of saving fuel and being economical who knows?

EIGHTEEN

Crabs and Shannocks

CRABS AND SHANNOCKS are the traditional names referring to the natives of Cromer and Sherringham, two small fishing towns in the county of Norfolk. This short story is dedicated to those people from whom I learnt a great deal and enjoyed a brief summer of picnicking by the beach, watching the sunset sky and, falling asleep to the sound of waves caressing the beach. Ah such romantic tosh!

For a short spell in my career I was posted – second class – to a small town on the Norfolk coast which delighted in a pier, a small railway station and a huge church and of course its crab fishermen and sundry extras.

Cromer was a typical English holiday town. As you swept down the brow of a hill toward the town you could see before you in a true Hardyesque landscape, a picture postcard of the tall flint knapped tower of the church dominating the skyline with the backdrop of the cold blue North Sea.

My bed and breakfast hotel overlooked the bay and in the early weeks so did my room. I would go to sleep to the constant rise and fall of the lighthouse beam bathing the walls and ceiling in a gentle pale light before fading into darkness. I was reminded of the novel "To The Lighthouse" by Virginia Woolf in which she very eloquently describes the effects of light and darkness emanating from the lighthouse beam. I wake to the sound of the waves crashing on the beach, and occasionally in the early hours of the morning by the crab fishermen setting sail on the morning tide, their small boats pitching in the waves until they became small specks amidst the fields of sea. The farmers of the ocean.

The beach was a wonderful place to sit, eat my tea and watch the sun go down and the moon rise over a grey translucent sea, a place to reflect and meditate and of course to promenade around that wonderful pier and glance up and the gothic Victorian hotel full of its ghosts of Edwardian society looking out to sea over their afternoon tea.

After breakfast, with an uninterrupted view of the council dustcart against the back drop of the sea, I left to travel the exceeding distance of two miles to get to the office. I will always remember the quality of light, the tang and smell of the sea which hit me as I left the front door. What better start to the day than that. Previously I had been working in Wakefield and the journey took me at least three hours per day, This was bliss. The bin men must have thought so too or they would not have parked their vehicle in such a prominent place

The office was a modern contraption designed by some ex- Islington architect who had gone native. Use had been made of the local knapped flint, a material the crab fishermen gathered from the shores during the winter months The building though grand in design unfortunately saved too much heat in summer and like a crab losing its shell sheds its heat in the winter months. The imitation sails hanging from the roof with their bright primary colours were a joy to see. The sails hung in great swathes from some ceilings gently swaying in the air currents. Was I in a medieval battle tent or a great banqueting hall? My brief was to inspect as many of the seasonal food shops as I could and I would plan a route and walk all day and return to the office in the evening.

My first visit was to a takeaway food shop. As I entered the premises my ears were immediately regaled by a Turkish band who appeared to be playing live from the pizza oven. I felt immense sorrow for the poor ears of the resident cockroaches in the oven. A full scale soccer match was also taking place on the television or was that coming from the storage area? An aromatic smell of Turkish coffee and pitta bread filled the kitchen as staff prepared breakfast.

Never one to say no to hospitality, I was asked if I would like some Turkish food. I of course accepted and stood eating and generally having a discussion on the ways of the world, occasionally having to refer to a Turkish-Norfolk English dictionary.

After eating it was time to have a look round. Most things were in order but as part of the new thinking of the joined up New Labour Government we were to ask questions about how and why certain aspects of the food business were carried out. Like, "why are you preparing food?" Now this is never a good thing to do and of course led to some really good explanations. I noticed that the staff were busy cleaning the food surfaces after breakfast and noted that the correct cleaning agents were being used. So I asked him why was he doing that task? He replied that it was to stop the stainless steel surface from going rusty. I was quiet for a while thinking, of that breakfast

I had been given and reached for my dictionary to translate the word "Gobsmacked," glanced sideways at the huge cleaver being used to cut the disinfected donna kebab and thought better of it.

The crab fishermen whom I described earlier would boil and dress their catch before selling them. Because the crabs were eaten they were subject to food regulations and had to be inspected. An area I knew very little about – there were some who would state very plainly that I knew very little anyway – so it was a question of visiting and, as I usually do, let the people tell me what they are doing and see if it sounded reasonable.

I remember my first visit clearly. It wasn't the hygiene side that caused the problem, it was the dialect. It was almost impossible to understand – I changed dictionaries from Turkish English to Norfolk English – what the man said but by sign language and powers of deduction I worked out how the operation was done. Yes there were rather large quantity of gas cylinders which seemed to be discarded randomly all around the site rather as if they had all gone down to the pub, returned, and fallen asleep where they stood. A huge stainless steel vat plus a quantity of crabs and lobsters indicated that somewhere along the line, the cylinders when sober would make friends with the stove who would heat the water into which the crabs would then jump to be cooked. Whilst the crabs looked a bit too stupefied to be that bothered the lobsters were still alive and enjoying the remainder of their life swimming in a container with their claws fastened. The lobsters were precious and kept alive and killed to order to preserve their freshness. I had never seen a live lobster and marvelled at the translucent blue colour of their shells. They looked very beautiful but dangerous, and given half a chance they would be on that tractor and back out to sea.

After their untimely death the crabs were taken from the place of execution to a place of their dressing. This was carried out by a relative of the fisherman who would dress them in all their Norfolk finery in a specially built room. Dressing a crab means the removal of the gills and intestines. I did soon start to realise that nearly everyone in the crab industry was related and one would act as interpreter for the rest. I soon found one person who I could understand – and he me – and, amidst the detritus of crab and lobster sandwiches I was regaled with the methods of catching the things and other tales of great adventure upon the high seas.

He told me of the history of the crab pot which was introduced from the north-east coast of England. The crab pot revolutionised the catching of

crabs. Until that time, crabs had been caught by hoop nets, baited and individually lowered into the water. The nets could be hauled fairly soon after lowering or would be buoyed and hauled after an hour or two. In either case it was a very slow catching technique.

The arrival of the crab pot allowed it to be left at sea from one day to the next, and would keep all the crabs and lobsters that entered for the "ment" – bait. The pots were called "swummers" at Sheringham and "floatums" at Cromer, seem to have been set and hauled individually but after a time the practice of setting a shank with several pots on it was developed.

One afternoon over tea and crab sandwiches I was told of one lobster that was so big the teller had a job wrestling it to the bottom of the boat. He had a job holding the claws apart to prevent being severely bitten. As this story was being unfolded his mother interspersed with "oh's" and "er's" as her knitting needles clicked as she made the traditional gansey and poured more tea which we all slurped noisily in eager anticipation of the next part of the story.

I came to realise that the art of crab dressing and boiling was like the moon it varied but to all intents and purposes it was fairly constant and so I ceased to worry about whether the population of Cromer and the surrounding area would die of a sudden bout of crab and lobster poisoning.

The mother told me a short story about the traditional gansey. A gansey is a navy blue woollen garment, worn by the fishermen locally. The gansey's are closely knitted and carry a distinctive pattern on their upper half. In the relative isolation local knitters copied and developed the patterns from each other and derived a style which was unique to their locality. It may have been possible to recognise local fishermen by the fabric patterns of their ganseys. There were no written patterns until about 1880. It was women and girls who earned money knitting up garments at home for merchants who supplied the wool. From research I know of one occasion in the nineteenth century when a drowned lifeboat man was identified by the individual weave of his socks made by his wife. (Source Radio Four. Programme on lifeboats).

As I left the house I remembered one thing. "If you sink at sea take your boots off!"

I could not help wondering if this practice would still be there in years to come. Boats left in remote bays were being damaged, their oars and rudders burnt on beach bonfires. These people were the old small holders of the sea with the custom of generation being handed down from generation to generation. Call me romantic but I am glad I got to know some of these people before some huge commercial conglomerate takes over.

I visited these people on a day of the total eclipse of the sun and somehow I feel that, like the return of the sun on that historical day, they will still be there. If not in person, in spirit, rising and falling in harmony on those field like waves in a way that only those in communication with nature can truly understand.

For notes I have referred to "Crabs and Shannocks, The Longshore Fishermen of North Norfolk," by Peter Stibbons, Katherine Lee and Martin Warren. Published by Poppyland Publishing 1983. ISBN 0 946148 02 3.

NINETEEN

The Red Rooster

FOR A SHORT spell after working in Cromer I went to an even smaller town called Havergo. Havergo in Suffolk was a new town, built as a result of the London overspill, although to be fair, before it was swamped it had been a small village with its characteristic pargetting and house fronts painted in gentle soft pastel colours which would glow in the early morning or evening sunlight.

When I arrived, the town was smarting over an article in the local newspaper that described it as a town full of either pregnant mum's or mum's pushing pushchairs followed by partners with very short hair and whose method of communication was by a mono syllabic grunt. I could see to some extent what the author had meant, but then there are always different sides to a town and when it is viewed on a damp wet day the view can be detrimental.

I was based in the council building built during the architectural period known as brutalism. Its new style of concrete blocks seemed harsh, although one thing in its favour it had a small area where children could play. On many an occasion I was sorely tempted to join in.

The office was fairly conservative and still had the morning round of the tea trolley, the operator of which, I still think of as the most powerful person in the entire council. Before I was unceremoniously made surplus to requirements in Sheeptown another member of the same genus existed and also exerted the same awe inspiring power; no doubt invoking the chief executive to rid her of that turbulent young Lewis who was always running off with her tea spoons. Come to think of it, I do have rather a large number, I must seek help. Tea and food ordered from the bakery were supplied in neat paper bags laid on the trolley with military precision. I wonder if there is a training college for such people? The tea and coffee came in delicate blue cups with saucers which in some ways was a counterpoint to the brutality of the building. It was during the usual debate over tea or "chi" that the days activities were discussed.

Some of our parishioners were being troubled by the sound of crowing hens very early in the morning and continuously during the day. Progress was slow and it was decided that the problem should be sorted once and for all. It was decided I was to spend some time in the morning and afternoon monitoring this problem. "And oh by the way." Said one of our more academic officers, "There is the smell problem from Skins You Like as well. Excellent we can send Stewart round to all the sites and he can monitor them." So it was the following routine; twenty minutes chickens, and twenty minutes on the smell, great all that time to sit and read or do whatever I needed to do.

First port of call the chickens. A suburban housing estate, the model of tranquillity. I could imagine John Betjeman composing his poems about such places – but oh, what danger lurks beneath the surface. I decided to sit outside in the sun have a cup of tea, listen and read my book. This was the life! I closed my eyes and felt the warm sun on my face. An occasional droning of a biplane flying overhead from the nearby Duxford flying museum – an excellent place to visit, in particular the workshops where you can see men and women working on the restored aeroplanes and smell the oil and lacquer used in the workshop – added to my stupor. I began dozing, my notebook gently slipped from my hands. Suddenly, my peace was shattered! It was though a red rooster behind the wooden fence had with its baton raised, shouted, "On the count of three." A cacophony of sound rent the gentle bird song. Was I dreaming or did I see a sparrow reach for its ear defenders and fly away and join the biplane.

Now my problem was how to record this. I noted that the cockerels were using a considerable amount of skill, or the conductor had gone for a tea break. There were altos, baritones and soprano's. Perhaps they had a cockerel tea trolley as well and it was time for a tea break. The noise of the crowing was either louder, fortissimo, or softer, pianissimo and then one would start mid range. Then there would be the longer crow or the shorter one. Perhaps some cockerels were more articulate than others I don't know.

At the time of writing up this story in Barnoldswick, England I can hear the sound of cockerels crowing in sympathy. But hark. Do I hear the flattened vowel of a Yorkshire type crow?

I decided it would be impossible to write down loud, soft crow etc as I would have difficulty in differentiating between them. And any way, I would without doubt be pulled to bits in a court of law. I decided to keep

little marks as the cockerels crowed and at the end of a period of time say constant or intermittent. As the noise continued I would have to forgo my rest and remain active. Oh well, never mind. I could still sit and watch the birds. As the time drifted on I began to differentiate between the cockerels and images of them strutting around being quiet one minute and then creeping up to the fence and making as loud a noise as possible. Perhaps using a megaphone? As the days went by I started to wonder if I was going native or was my imagination playing tricks. Perhaps I would end up going up to the fence and start berating them for their strange behaviour. It would end up that the cockerels starting up their own petition against a noisy Environmental Health Officer!

My final destination was of an olfactory nature. Havergo was unfortunate in that on its windward side it had a number of factories which could cause a smell. There was the chemical plant "Pongos," the flavouring plant "Exotico" and the skin manufactures "Skins You Almost Like." Because Havergo was expanding, the houses were being built in close proximity to the factory units. On this particular assignment, my nose, with the aid of transport, was to be placed in different parts of the district to detect the smells and also make note of the weather conditions.

The most interesting visit was outside "Skins You Almost Like." It consisted of a small number of industrial units. The occupants of these units were complaining that from time to time they were quite literally smelt out of their work along with their customers. Of course, it is always the case that when you arrive there is no smell and everyone comes out and says that it was worse before you arrived, when you left and at the same time yesterday. Of course I wasn't there at those times as I was trying to visit randomly. So I sat and listened to Radio Four which is a godsend. I listened to Fergal Kean and Frank McCourt with their Irish lilts telling stories about life. I envied their story telling abilities. Kean for the sadness that his stories of alcoholism brought to me and McCourt for well, just being himself, "Tiss" but a story, a yarn.

Then things started to happen... Not a smell but other activities...

There was one unit which always seemed very empty but on this particular morning became very busy. A man pulled up and very serepticiously got out of his car and rang a bell. He was greeted by a lady with a pronounced limp who let him in.

After about 30 minutes he left in much the same way as he had come in.

The whole process was repeated several times. The sandwich man looked suspicious but may be that was something to do with the food!

Now of course you can not sit in a car for all that time day in and day out without becoming noticed. I had become friendly with a couple who ran an engineering workshop called "Nut and Bolt." They were from the Black Country and very friendly. It was often difficult to know if they were in, as they seemed not to like the sun and kept the door closed.

One day I knocked and over a brew discussed the merits of the work they were undertaking. We got round to discussing the activities of our lady next door. "Oh that." He said between slurps of tea... and he got an article from one of the Sunday papers and showed me this buxom blond posing in front of a leopard. The oil stained fingers grasping the paper gave the article a very down to earth feel. "She poses for customers with that thing over there and gets paid more than I do. She sometimes calls for a coffee to discuss the torque rating of the chains. An ex-engineer you know. More money." The photographs showed a blond woman in various salacious poses with another genetically cloned blond girl wrestling with a leopard. The leopard looked very still and sad, mind you, wouldn't you if you had to be mauled by a blond tigress and smelt out by "Skins You Almost Like?" I think the leopard longed to return to the wild savanna of the Oxfam shop.

There is a motto here. Think very carefully before you take your stuffed toy to the Oxfam shop as you never know where it might end up. "Oh by the way," said Mr Bolt, "I once did some welding for her." He scratched his head as his wife looked on interested. "That's it some chains, heavy duty." He thought better of saying any more and returned to contemplate a small delicately ground piece of engineering.

So a visit to "Skins You Almost Like" became quite interesting watching the comings and goings. The white BMW outside denoted that materially there was some monetary gain there.

Did the smells get sorted? I don't know. Did the leopard escape? The saga continues.

TWENTY

Life – not as we know it – on the Old Kent Road, London

This short story is dedicated to all those children of Southwark who brighten up a concrete landscape from which they have little escape.

A Trilogy

Part One
A Night On The Town

AFTER A SHORT but meaningful spell in the Black Country, definitely not Birmingham – where according to one West Indian lady, "De rats so confident dey walk across de lawn like dey got de rent book" – I applied for work through an agency and was given an assignment or was it an assignation to go and try my hand at working with a local authority noise team in deepest South London.

"Have you done any noise work?" Asked a lady with a name more reminiscent of a heroine in the French resistance?"

"A bit in Sheeptown." I replied.

"Come on down," she said, "you'll do."

The office was a converted car park with a huge block of flats towering above it. The car park had been too dangerous to place cars in it so they had taken the safer option and placed humans in it instead. Entry out of hours was by a metal roller shutter which you sometimes had to bang on in order to get in – a fine example of noise prevention. Every window had a mesh grill. The grim appearance of the place was only broken by the colour and sound of the local West Africans; they wore a brilliant array of colours and that was just on their heads!

The children were small islands of colour amidst the drab surroundings of what appeared to be a never ending suburbia of high rise flats. Sometimes a splash of yellow caught my eye, not flowers but signs erected by the police asking if there were any witnesses to a recent robbery or stabbing. I remember walking to work one day and seeing a child standing in a bus shelter with his mother. The early morning sun with its clarity gave the child and his bright wondrous eyes, clothes and rucksack, a vivid tableaux of colour.

The noise team worked on a twenty four hour shift system which meant that you could be working all night. A feeling of dread overcame me, I had never worked all night. Could I stay awake? I was soon to find out.

At night the office could be very quiet until the phone rang and out you went, complete with security officer, in an environmentally friendly gas propelled car. The staff were great fun to work with. Conversation revolved around many and varied topics when the telephone went quiet. Jamaicans told of their cure for the common cold and all other ailments as "the weed" which they would never be without. Not forgetting the obligatory Jamaican rum. I remember one evening we received a telephone call from a person complaining of noisy children. "Aint you got no kids of your own," the receptionist said, "Give de mother a break, and ring back if they trouble you after nine." I was aghast. After all my training I would never speak to a person like that. This was indeed a strange world.

So, it came to pass, the dreaded night shift, Saturday, one of the busiest nights in the week. In the event I didn't have time to even think about sleeping. Even the adrenaline was afraid of relaxing.

I was on my shift with a fellow health officer. I shall call her Miss Green Mittens, for no other reason than she used a green fountain pen and wore fingerless mittens; good for keeping your hands warm and at the same time having your fingers free to write notes. Miss GM – not as far as I am aware genetically modified – had a fierce reputation of marching in to difficult situations and solving the problem there and then. Some inspectors wondered how she did it, risking life and limb. But then she got away with it, perhaps, because of her confidence. We had received a complaint about a rave party taking place in a disused warehouse. The police were anxious to stop the event before it got under way.

Down some ill-lit street we ventured and found the venue. We could even hear the noise long before we reached the site. We went inside to speak to the organisers, up a staircase and into what I can only describe as an empty storage area. In one corner of a gloomy room was a glowing gas cylinder heater, its flame singeing anyone who got too near it. No one had seemed to take into consideration the plastic camouflage netting draped overhead to divide one side of the room. If this netting caught fire there would be a disaster. Rave goers were drifting in and I was surprised at the number of people already there. I am not afraid to state that I was scared. There were only the two of us and one police sergeant, though admittedly there were about five coach loads of police outside. A considerable amount of damage could be done to us in a very short space of time before they arrived on the scene.

Downstairs was in virtual darkness apart from a few precariously hung light bulbs, their harsh glare showing the only toilet perched at a dangerous angle amidst rubble and broken timber beams. The emergency escape route was not even visible. I had never seen anything quite like this before.

A legal notice was served to tell the occupiers not to cause a noise nuisance and they were also told that their equipment would be seized should the need arise. Now this is a powerful incentive as often the equipment is the most valuable thing in the building. The music was turned off and I was surprised that once the music stopped the people just seemed to melt away. Eventually we received another call and left leaving several shadowy riot vans full of recumbent police officers no doubt extremely bored.

Our next visit was to another rave or proposed one which the police had got wind of. The interesting thing about this rave was that the persons who had gained entry to the building had not forced an entry and therefore had not broken the law. The idea was that the organisers get several lorries full of drink set up an illegal party on the premises and advertise the event on the internet, by word of mouth or by mobile 'phones. They obviously make a quick killing not having to pay for the venue. A knock on the door revealed two organisers named Jack and Jill. In between them there appeared to be a gormless individual who just looked at us and smiled. The usual banter was exchanged as witnessed by several van loads of even more police officers. By this time their helmets were of more use as pillows. Jack and Jill seemed to take the hint and may have gone back down the hill for we did not hear of any further difficulties.

Back to the fortress for a break. I telephone ahead to say we were safe – we always rang in to report our movements never giving the exact address in case any one was listening on the mobile 'phone network or we could have had unexpected guests. We also rang to tell our colleagues to be ready to open the drawbridge. The fortress was opened and we went upstairs and put the kettle on taking care not to wake the staff who take the calls, as in quiet moments they were of a mind to put their heads down rather like the police officers. The only creatures not sleeping were the cockroaches, which, we were told, could crawl all over your food if you left it out. If the 'roaches didn't get your food someone else would, for there was also a thief about.

On reflection I had noticed how my colleague would become visibly excited if we received notice of a big noise problem. She would get extremely agitated as we sped from one complaint to another. At one point I became very anxious as we turned the car round and cut up several Nigerians in a car – it was rumoured that most of them didn't have licenses – they stopped the car and looked at us in a very menacing way. Miss Green Mittens looked back at them with such a contemptuous stare that they thought better of it and sped away, their blaring music melting into the cacophony of what is the Old Kent Road on a Saturday night.

The Old Kent Road at two o clock in the morning is as nothing I have ever seen. There are masses of people in various states of intoxication, ambulances, police with their horns blaring, cars tearing up and down in what I can only describe as bedlam as their deep bass music thudded and pulsed, the occupants' dark shadows jerking to the music inside. It was a very exciting bedlam and an atmosphere which is not conducive to sleep at all. Going into a burger bar to get some food for my driver, I was very conscious of being the only person waiting to be served who was not drunk.

We cruise down the Old Kent Road passing Henry Cooper's old boxing gym – The Thomas A'Becket – and following the Canterbury Pilgrims. Never in my wildest dreams could I have imagined being here doing this work when twenty years before my family had used the very same route to go down to our house in Kent. Life indeed can be very strange. The telephone beeped as our next call came. A rave under the railway arches at London Bridge. Green Mittens was now completely fired up. At approximately a half mile away we could hear the dull thud of the bass beat. She gripped the steering wheel harder with her fingerless mittens and stabbed down on the gas. Arriving on the scene the noise was echoing down the starkly lit canyons of the arches. A police officer met us saying that it was a lot quieter now. In fact, when he had gone to the venue, he had nearly been knocked off his feet from the noise.

So, on foot, we went to speak to the organisers who were most reluctant

to let us in. We were not too bothered as the evening was coming to a close anyway. As we stood at the doorway it became apparent why they did not want us to go in. Dark shadowy figures were drifting past wearing what appeared to be just overcoats and clutching plastic bags with various articles of clothing hanging out. It turned out to be a fetish ball and evidently anything went. I regret to say that even in the case of being authorised officers of the council and Sam Pepys – myself – wanting copy for his story we were still not let in!

On our return to the office the sky around London Bridge was lit up with the inferno of a paper mill alight. Huge orange flames leapt skywards. The flames throwing into sharp relief the jumble of other buildings. Tonight it was really all happening, a night that I will not forget.

Around 4.00 am things seemed to calm down, reports were written up and it was time to wind down. I went out onto a form of balcony which overlooked the entrance. It was surrounded by a cage to prevent intruders getting in. Together with one of our security men we drank coffee and in quiet contemplation watched the awakening of another day. The streets as though exhausted with the nights activities were quiet and still. There was a calm about the place, time for a period of reflection.

Part Two
The Schizophrenic

THE WORK OF the noise team can be very stressful One of the main causes of stress is never knowing who or what is on the other side of the door when you visit. This can apply equally when visiting a complainant or the person complained about, as this short story will illustrate.

One evening we received a call from a local police station referring to a gentleman who had called in to make a complaint about a neighbour making a noise. The request was that we visit in half an hour. The time it would take him to get home. The police had also remarked that this gentleman did seem a little strange.

A visit was made to a high rise building. The lift smelt strongly of disinfectant and urine, the harsh light bouncing off the metal corrugated sides. As we walked along the passageway to the flat I could see the lights of Tower Bridge, the bridge my brother used to call "The Breaking Up Bridge," as we passed over it on our way south to visit one of my fathers properties in Gravesend, Kent. The city lights shimmered and showed a black void where the river flowed. The wind howled through the metal fire doors. We counted the numbers and doors, mostly fitted with grills in front of them. Small fortresses within a fortress. I thanked my lucky stars I usually lived in the north within sight of the countryside, what a terrible way of life.

We reached the door of the complainant and knocked. A late middle-aged man answered the door and we went inside. The demeanour of the man was of subservience, his head was down and he looked very meek. He wore a tie and was reasonably attired. He complained of a noise from the floor above. We are only allowed to take action if we can hear a noise which in our view is a nuisance. On this occasion we could hear nothing. One of the hazards of the job in visiting a complainant is not hearing the noise; maybe the person has seen you coming or switched off the offending noise. This can lead to an extreme amount of frustration and, when it is coupled with a loss of sleep can be very stressful. We of course had to tell the man we could not hear the noise at the time and if it did re-occur we would come back. As my companion was telling him this he suddenly became extremely agitated and on the verge of violence. His whole attitude towards us changed to such an extent that we had to immediately leave the premises.

As we left we could hear the man shouting, "I will burn the fuckers out," before he slammed the door, the noise echoing down the corridors. We reached the lift and made toward the ground floor. My companion, extremely experienced in noise work was shaken. The unexpected turned upside down, I dread to think if one of us had been there alone, never before had a urine soaked lift been so welcome!

Part Three
A Seizure

IN THE EXTREME cases the noise team is allowed with the permission of a magistrate to enter a property and seize equipment, records, compact discs and tapes.

This particular raid was, as you would expect, carried out at dawn with the assistance of the police and one very large van in which to place the equipment to be taken. I then heard that our target had recently been in prison for being in possession of a knife. This fact thrilled me immensely. We had all been measured for stab vests but they had yet to be delivered. Our briefing was precise and each person knew their allocated tasks. One was to remove the goods whilst another was to stay with the van and the other person to talk to the suspect. Another high rise block of flats, always tricky, as you do not know who else is in the building and whether a major disturbance could be sparked off as a result of our visit and subsequent actions. Balconies are also a problem; you are always advised to keep to the side of the building. It's further to throw you over the side! Down below us are several wrecked cars and a railway track running past us on which the occasional suburban service rattles through. This is metroland without the flowers.

We have met the police before and have agreed tactics. One officer is to go to the door with a police constable. Around a corner are reinforcements, myself and a locksmith. We knock at the door. The sound echoes around the walls and corridor, and out into nothingness. The atmosphere is tense. Then the door opens, the situation is explained by the constable and suddenly it is closed again. What do we do? Has he gone for a weapon? Do we break in and overpower the said suspect? After what appears to be an age the door re-opens. "How can a guy let you in when he has no trousers on?" He shouts as he proceeds to let us in and then goes to the toilet, leaving the door open. He returns, zipping up his trousers and we explain why we have come. The police making sure that he sits down, that way it is easier to control him. At first he does not appear to mind too much when we take his hi-fi. Then when we start to take his records and tapes he gets more agitated, he starts to rise, the room feels extremely small considering there are two noise officers, two policemen and the guy himself. If he decides to pull a knife or throw a punch there is not a great deal of room in which to escape. I am not paid for being sick either - one of the perks of being an agency worker. I am given a pile of records and thankfully make toward the van as quickly as I can.

At last all is removed, then to the dismay of the occupier the police search the property and find the electricity meter has been bypassed. As we leave in the van the tenant is seen being led away arrested and handcuffed. Not only has he lost his records, some of them valuable but is discovered to be bypassing the electricity meter. Not a good hair day.

Back at the office I spend the entire day sitting on an upturned red bucket wearing my red hat in a freezing cold room writing down all the names of the records. One staff member says I look a picture. As I sit, shiver and write, I reflect that dawn raids do have their more boring side!.

TWENTY-ONE

Sand Grown

THE RAW BEAT of music rose and fell around me with the steady frequency of the waves crashing against the shore. Small figures skittered along the front avoiding the occasional tumultuous wave which would soak their only means of warmth, a brightly coloured shirt which denoted summers by appearance only. The women, clinging to their partners, tottered along on their high heels.

I walked back to my car feeling exhilarated, the wind whipping against my face, everything was new and exciting. I glanced up to where people were being hurled into space by a machine which appeared to have the capacity to ensure that your breakfast would take at least several nanoseconds to catch up with your stomach. A young girl danced with her feet to an intricate music machine which, as it increased in tempo demanded that her foot movements also increase. Mesmerized, I stood entranced at the sophistication of the steps. Reflecting on this I suddenly realised that it was a mechanical form of hopscotch played in isolation. The music machine taking the place of friends chanting in the playground. The arcade representing the exchange of private space for public, the feeling of safety but at a price. We pay in more ways than one for our pleasures now.

At last I turned into the road where my car was parked. Time for my usual sandwiches, a flask of coffee and a quick write up of my notes from the mornings visit to ascertain the food hygiene standards of the emporiums of Blackdale. As I walked along repeating the phrase "sandwiches, coffee, sandwiches, coffee" it dawned that I could not see my car. "Damn and crumbs!" – the extent of my bad language had somehow never got beyond private school – I must have parked it somewhere else. Not only was I starting to talk to myself but I was forgetting where I had parked the car. I walked on unconcerned as my memory was so well dis-established that it was not such an uncommon occurrence. Only yesterday I had placed my mobile telephone in a fridge to ascertain its temperature instead of my thermometer! The look on the fridge owner's face registered a mix between sympathy and abject terror. It was at that moment that I decided to call it a day and go home.

After much searching, and a refusal to believe the obvious I began to realize that my car was not there. My mind still refused the obvious, no... it could not have been stolen. After all, who would want to steal such an old machine, my brother's first company car. Now, transport wise, he is on to better things such as an old Landrover, so old it is not a legal necessity to fit seat belts! But stolen the car was. I rang the police – praising, for once the mobile telephone – and started to get my mind into gear. How was I going to get home with no money and no coat?

Now reader, have you ever been accosted at some train or bus station by a person asking for the fare home, as they had been robbed? You thought, "oh yea, pull the other one," and ignore them. Well, it had happened to me, and someone else to whom I had related the story. It gives you an interesting perspective on life. I stammered out my story to the train conductor who, to his credit, got out of a difficult situation by stating that the train may be decrepit but it could take a switch money card. Amazingly, I could pay my way home after all! The guard was also sympathetic since he had had his motorbike stolen recently. Throughout the rackety journey I kept thinking that the car was parked somewhere else and that at any moment the police would ring me to call me a stupid twit who had parked his car in the wrong place. They never did.

I settled back to think of the day's events, as the often unsung beauty of the Lancashire countryside rattled past the window. I had visited a hotel where the proprietor, sitting in her little office with a portable slot machine television, had inquired if I was "sand grown." This of course floored me – it doesn't take a lot – until she explained that she was asking if I was born in Blackdale with its miles of sand, and therefore sand grown. I explained that I was "Thames grown" and in fact my parents had picked me up out of the river Thames as a piece of salvage and had bound me up in an oiled sailcloth, kept me in a shed built of driftwood in an orchard that belonged to my Grandfather in a place called Swanscombe. My parents had been forced into this action because my date of birth was very nearly calculated as being out of wedlock and until such facts could be confirmed, my fate was to lay in an orchard in secret. Luckily, all worked out well but the smell of the gentle scent of maturing apples reminds me of that secretive time.

As the journey continued I thought of another hotel I had visited that day when I was confronted by an Irishman who, on seeing me as he jumped in front of some decrepit plaster work, proclaimed, "put a name in the pot." Thinking I was about to be the subject of some Irish ritual, I became a little concerned for my safety. This Irishman had a gleam in his eye and seemed to be standing at a considerable slant with the effect that he was almost leaning over me. I played along in my usual fashion of remaining cool and tried not to antagonise him too much until I too found myself almost crashing into the kitchen sink and colliding with the pot in which my name was to be ritually boiled. "It's a fair slant." He said clinging to the cupboard in the way of a seaman in a force ten. "It's the sand, we are all sliding into the sea." A casual glance at the top of the door showed a slant of considerable proportions and a door which had not been closed for a good few years. "Now then want a cup of tea?" I almost cried in relief, I was not to be boiled alive but offered a cup of tea and this was the Irish way of greeting people. As I sipped my tea compensating myself against the slant, I reflected on how again I had learnt more of life's richness than environmental health matters.

A screech of brakes and a gentle thud indicated that end of the line had been reached. Bonny Clogg Heads, once a railway terminus of considerable size, was now reduced to a single dead end line. You can almost sense the feeling of sadness and neglect as you descend onto a once proud paved platform which played host to direct trains to London and Sheeptown.

Now this is where the euphoria fades. I found it rather like after a car crash. One had survived! I had got home and felt the sudden loss of energy as I realised the implications of my loss and the shock from it. Of course I had to ring up my boss at Blackdale as all my blank inspection forms were in the car, together with a white coat and hat. Some weird individual could easily try to pass himself as a health official. I can not think of a reason why. Ian Walnut, one of the senior inspectors, was very helpful. "Perhaps they might do some inspections for us." was his laconic reply. "I thought you had something more serious to report. Come to think of it you are the only one to have this occur." I thought to explain that these problems always found me but stopped and thought better of it. I was, of course more devastated by the loss of my out of print book on an eccentric archaeologist. In fact the insurance company started to get a little concerned when they realised how badly affected I was by the loss.

So life settled down to a routine of hire cars and borrowing my father's "tank" which, when my mother was alive she would aim rather than drive.

I remember a story about her eating a bacon sandwich at some traffic lights, when a policeman gestured for her to wind down her window. He asked her if she was OK eating the sandwich in the car. "Oh yes," she replied. "I am fine. The sandwich is good too." She then realised that the policeman had other ideas as to the driving ability of "The Queen" as she was affectionately called.

So, it came to pass that the telephone rang and a voice whispered to me in a very conspiritorial manner, "We have found your car but we don't know where it is. You have to ring 'Fred' to find out the location." This all sounded mysterious and rather upsetting as I had begun to look forward to getting a new car and didn't want the hassle of repairing the stolen one. I rang "Fred." Another dismembered voice rustled a few papers and at last confirmed that he had indeed booked a certain car into his huge log book. My next contact was based in Liverpond. With trepidation I rang yet another number. "Liverpond Crash 'em or Nick 'Em Cars here," answered a voice as thick as treacle but with particles of sand in it, probably from Blackdale. The voice though was friendly. Yes they had the car, it was clearly recognisable by all the papers in it, quite unusual, did I want to come over? "Well whack you take the first corner on the right after Elmtree, go left at the guy selling hash, at the next corner look out for the garage, but take care, park with care." As I put the 'phone back I was sure I could hear the sound of extra voices echoing so take care or some-one else will.

I set off and navigated my way to the 'pond following my hastily scribbled instructions. Spot on as I recognised the sign, "Crash 'Em or Nick 'Em." Investors in people. Qualified to ISO 8000. Winners of the Plain English Award. Courses on hot wiring, crash recovery and a host of other aspects were offered The obligatory www. crash 'em. co. uk. confirmed that the internet boom had even reached Liverpond. In the garage were groups of very donnish oil clad men in gowns with text books in their hands and spanners behind their ears discussing different aspects of car maintenance, the repair of cars, the art of starting without turning the ignition and various aspects, of getting into a car without a key. I relaxed for a moment as I observed that at least spanners were de rigour behind the ear rather than a mobile phone. My revelry was shattered by a round of applause and the slapping of hands on oil stained overalls as one student exclaimed stopwatch in hand "0.5 seconds wack, a new record to get into a car!" I was warmly received in this garage of learning as no doubt my car would be another teaching aid to the students. My ID presented, an extremely important looking book was handed to me by oil stained but dexterous fingers. The ledger coloured by differing qualities of oil staining reflecting its age and authenticity.

The deed was done and off I went to see my car for the last time. On my way out my attention was drawn to a book on a chair. It read, "A Dissertation on the Quantum Mechanics of Applying Unspecified Force To Mechanical Objects." Truly this was an amazing place!

My car was left in a corner rather like some wallflower at a dance neglected and alone. It was surrounded by other lost and forlorn vehicles maimed beyond redemption. Its remarkable appearance confirmed that I had not left the door unlocked but that someone with an expert knowledge had used keyhole surgery to drill a neat hole through the left hand door lock and, hey presto they were in and away. I sighed and to some extent felt relieved that my absent mind had not extended to forgetting to lock the door. I wondered what the eminent mechanical professors would have declared about the work. Would they mechanically deconstruct the work and declare it to be post modern or reject it as brutalism with regard to the more refined modernist methods. The car was exactly as left. All my notes were there, a despairing banana skin lay forlornly on the floor, it's only companion a flask still containing three week old coffee. On the rear seat my chirpy "Mortimer Wheeler" book, the glint seemed to say in the author's eyes, "the bounders – he was of a bygone age – would not dare to take me away." Come to think of it who in their right mind would choose to steal an out of date book on a dead archaeologist?

It felt like stripping a corpse of all its belongings. Dead. The company car which had been at the beginning of the LEWIS Communications empire and had seen me through some turbulent times was to be no longer. I removed the contents into a black bin bag and left.

As I walked back to my hire car I felt a small movement come from within the bag. Not everything had died!!!

TWENTY-TWO

When East Meets West

THIS IS A cautionary tale – in part – of how we all from time to time allow others to colour our opinions and subsequent actions toward those we are about to meet or have not met.

My time was up. I was to be transferred. A full time job at last, although I think an arrangement of several meat and pork pies had been agreed to help the deal along namely from my colleagues who had dispaired of my inept tea making faculties – note: not my ability to do the job! The venue, a Stalinist building which can be found anywhere in this country and are so people friendly that they have to have bars on the windows to prevent the members of the public from gaining entry.

"Be warned!" My colleagues had said of "The Tzar," who rules with a rod of iron, and to whom smiling is an anathema. Everyone working there is dying to get out and few do. "The Tzar" was the legendary figure presiding over the so called "Hammer House Of Horror" which was situated in the gloomy valley named Doom Kirk. Folk lore was that the local monks had smashed down their own abbey and blamed it on Henry VIII to get out of the area. It was that bad.

The so called "Hammer House of Horror" had the appearance of a Gothic villa. The building was presided over by a forlorn eagle which had been frozen in stone by a magical mouse which lived within the building. It had got fed up with all its friends and family being terrorised by the eagle swooping on them like some medieval dive bomber.

As I drove up to it that morning the only light came from the yellowing windows, the light fighting a losing battle with the all encompassing gloom of the valley. From behind those windows could be seen small thin bent figures moving about.

Upon arrival I nearly tripped over a huge concrete block laying amidst wooden debris on the floor. Another break in I was told. The thieves had removed the outer security bars and smashed their way in. In one area they had broken a door which was already open. The computers had been targeted. I was amazed at the number they had taken before the security people had arrived. Mind you, as some wag remarked, we do have our opening hours on the door.

I was shown into an office complete with swing doors which looked more akin to some western saloon bar. I wondered how many inspectors had been thrown out for not completing their targets of premises to inspect. As I entered drunken computers lay on the floor their main arteries severed. Amidst the carnage a sign said "Scene Of Crime, Do Not Touch!" If my memory served me well I think the sign stayed until our comrades returned to steal the remainder.

Inside the building were wonderful wall tiles and ornate fireplaces that echoed a past life of decadence. I was already beginning to feel cowed by the building in the way my masters wanted. The staircase was so huge and wide that staff could be seen and examined for their cultural honesty at least five minutes before you drew closer to them. The bannister offers a wonderful opportunity to slide down. I had heard of rumours that on nights of the full moon "The Tzar" would along with his cat slide down the bannister waving the red flag and the cat singing along to the tune of "The Red Flag."

I was admitted to the inner sanctum. "The Tzar" jumped to his feet and informed me I was too early. A look which would have been sufficient for the spiders inhabiting the office to decide to leave on an extended holiday. The cat purring on the desk looked at me with eyes that said breakfast is early. I cowered before my new boss and sat meekly in the corner. His eyes drilled into me, tell me about yourself – if there is anything worth telling – which time zone do you come from? I explained that I had come from a distant authority where inspectors were happy and, oh time was a non linear progression as far as I was concerned. As I spoke I felt as thought the time theory was beginning to work as I felt the earth sliding from beneath me and the chair on which I was sat leaned alarmingly, nearly pitching me into a giant banner depicting striding young men and women marching with computer sets held aloft in their strong arms.

He started to talk about sandwiches and explained where to go to purchase such commodities. A brief introduction was given about the fire drill to be followed in the event of an emergency. Then I saw it, like the sparkle of a shinning gun barrel in Red Square, a four leaf clover, it appeared and disappeared – a smile, as he reflected his pride in his work as he informed me curtly that if the fire did not get you the traffic would.

Before I was allowed to leave I was shown the wide window ledges offering a standing room view of Doom Kirk. I was informed that decadent comrades who failed to reach their inspection targets are offered the opportunity to sit on them and admire the view before they are pushed off to re educate them. I thought to myself that I would not dare do such a thing without at least sending a memorandum to my line manager – in triplicate!

I could not wait to tell my colleagues that I had witnessed such an event. As I left he called out, "Before you go remember never set foot in the wrong time zone." I looked at him in bewilderment. He continued, "We are divided here into the western zone and the eastern zone. You are in the eastern zone and never, never cross the line of demarcation." He pointed to the middle of the office. Just as a member of staff appeared to have skipped over an imaginary object. I nodded as I left the office and wondered whether I would ever be able to escape. As I left I noticed the clock on the other side of the office read 10.00am. Strange I was sure that the clock above his door had said 8.00am as I went in. I glanced back to the area from which I had emerged. "The Tzar" sat over his computer. Was he plotting the downfall of western society. Was that a hammer and sickle I could see as a screen saver on his computer quietly playing the "The Red flag?"

Eventually I was released and slunk into my desk directly under "The Tzars" flight path. Unfortunately even if the wind was in another direction his approach was the same. I could only pray for fog or the Fifth Cavalry. Mind you the cavalry was so prone to killing the wrong side I thought better of it. As I sat gently sipping tea and shaking like a road traffic victim. An office member sidled up to me and whispered a welcome as they glanced furtively toward the inner sanctum and scurried away to their desks, their heads burrowed beneath piles of regulations and orders proclaiming this and that to be an imminent health hazard to the great populous of Doom Kirk.

Luckily I was not without friends. A member of staff whom I shall give the code name of "Canario." "Canario" had offered to make me a brew and by a secret chirping indicated that she sometimes spoke to others in the western sector. Those in the western sector were seen as decadent and not pulling their weight when carrying out inspections.

I sat at my desk I immediately felt to be in another time zone. Whilst sipping my brew I wondered if my friend Yip had exerted some form of "feng shui" over the office. Yip was a health officer who believed in alternative health remedies and also had a mind of his own.

I was to work in the eastern sector and automatically assumed the role of my boss as hard and ruthless inspector inspecting premises with an ice like precision..

I started to settle in but trouble was never far away – strange – but it never is as far as I am concerned.

One day I entered the office to be confronted by "The Tzar" complete with a shining rapier which he had retained from his days as a cavalry officer. It was being swished around in the air with a menacing purpose. As the swishing continued he approached my good self. I froze. Death by a rapier, I had not thought of that one. Death by sharpened drain rod covered in sewage, but that, no. At least it was more romantic and would make better copy in the Environmental Health Magazine, also known lovingly as "Specimen News." The headline would read, "Turbulent Health Inspector Run Through." As the blade became nearer I saw that there was an object attached to the point which looked rather brown and dripping. My heart froze, had already got someone through the heart and it was still steaming? My life slowly flashed before me – remember I was at work!

As my failing eyes focused on the object I realised that it was a wet steaming tea bag. The tea bag left a vapour trail as it dripped on the very expensive pile carpet in our office which had just been re laid in the Western Sector thanks to some money received from the National Lotto who had agreed with Councillor Diddleem that they were a good cause. A good cause for what I am not sure. The only problem was the burglars who were frequent visitors never wiped their feet. The poor old caretakers are forever on their hands and knees cleaning. If there was a good cause it is them, the unsung heroes.

As the staff looked on the only sound was the methodic swishing. Short sharp words broke the silence. "Comrade Lewis, you have been using the Peoples tea bags, the penalty is to be made a fool of in front of the entire office." A shudder went around the assembled group. Dan Dan the sailor man who, tired of a tea bag in every port and happy to be in the green and peaceful landscape of Doom Kirk, visibly winced and his eyes welled up with the salt of the oceans. He had once been the subject of such a tirade and knew the abject terror that it invoked. He would have welcomed the cat o' nine tails any day.

Suddenly the swishing sound was broken by a tremendous crash as the

BAZ.

saloon doors burst open and the boss Greenwich Meridian came in or rather staggered in. He had forgotten that the doors only opened one way – to throw people out. All eyes turned and unfortunately so did "The Tzar" who was still swishing and had lost sight of his trajectory such as it was that the tea bag detached itself from the sword and entered into orbit. It was able to do this because of the extreme height of the ceiling. All eyes followed the bag as it reached its parabolic height, pierced several spiders webs and started on its downward flight trajectory. All the combined efforts of NASA and the Russian space programme could not have planned a better landing site for the re-entry of the orbital tea bag. Tea bag – beep, simulated landing, beep – as the shining forehead of "GM" came into contact. There was no parachute or afterburner to slow the descent and impact was considerable. The tea bag hit his forehead and slid down his nose followed by a slowly running brown viscous liquid.

Shock horror! Was this the end of "The Tzar"? Would he no longer brew his tea bags at 1.7°c seconds recurring, would the black cat join the effigy of the eagle on the roof? Would Stewart or Sid the Tea Boy as he was now affectionately known be transferred again? Each member of staff had, no doubt, their own thoughts but GM had none of it. He appeared to be deeply troubled by something. That something was a piece of paper in his hand which was showing a slight degree of staining Was it peace in our time? As GM regains his dignity, for he is a big cheese within the department, and tries to look calm, he wipes his head with a handkerchief which was so well ironed it looked as though it might decapitate him. He informs us of a food complaint which may have very serious repercussions for the department. We all paused...

"Staff." He declared. "McGlory the decadent food manufactures have produced a run of 10.000 of these." He showed us a photograph of a chicken head in batter which had just arrived via the world wide web. Beneath the picture the text read McGlory head'n'fries for 10 cents, eyes for free to see you all through the week. "Was this a wind up?" Dan asked. For he had seen much upon his travels. "No." GM declared, I will make a decision without a committee. This is definitely the real thing – pun – McGlory had taken on a public relations firm of "Soften 'Em Up" to reduce the impact. All heads were to be collected and sent to a deserving third world country. Unfortunately there was a further problem with the galactic interface of the WASP information system and that country is... Britain.

We must treat this matter as urgent. Let's put the kettle on!

"The Tzar" jumped up-after drinking his tea at 63.7°, tannin brown and swung his rapier. "Up and at 'em he declared. Our corporate mission statement is to save the human race from this filth." He burst through the swing doors and slid down the bannister before disappearing with the staff behind him. In the distance could be heard a dull crash and horns sounding. He had forgotten the traffic!

Alone in the office sat myself and the cat who glanced at me in a sly way and sipped his delicious whipped cream done to purr-fection at 63.9°. He might just tell "The Tzar" to stir and not shake the mixture in the future.

Apart from the gentle purring of a very contented cat could be heard a staccato beep coming from one of the computers that had been mortally wounded which even the thieves had not thought worth stealing. "Beep" it went, "beak n'fries, beak n'fries 10 cents including beak, buy now no…" Beep bong. System failure, the computer proclaimed. "It's not my fault!"

Now my story could well end here, but you will recall the beginning of this tale and my encounter with "The Tzar" so read on…

Time passed with irregularity. Remember we possess two time zones in one office. "The Tzar" became affected by global detente. The turning point came when a colleague mentioned caviar. It was the custom that if any officers made a mistake they had to buy the rest of the staff caviar as a punishment. This was a trap to which my good self had fallen into many times.

I seem to remember the the word was spoken in a fairly soft tone for most conversations in the office are whispered. Within seconds The Tzar had emerged from his office, eyes ablaze and sword at the ready. "Did I hear the word caviar? I do love caviar and vodka." I can hear the word with accuracy of a well bugged telephone. Or I seemed to recall it was some distance involved with duelling. As he uttered the word he threw an imaginary bottle and caviar up into the void of the office ceiling. The caviar landed ready on to a plate which had appeared in his other hand. His eyes glinted and a smile appeared as he returned to the inner sanctum. A few moments later the sound of laughter could be heard along with the sound of a gentle purr.

There followed a period of calm within the building. The red flag disappeared and inspectors were no longer taken to the window sill for a failure to reach targets and buy caviar. "The Tzar" appeared to relax; talk of cabbages and kings with both sectors. He no longer seemed as aware of the decadence or excess of the comrades. All was in harmony.

The motto of this story is, beware the judgement of others until you have made up your own mind and opinion.

Afterthought

IN NOVEMBER 2002 whilst writing this book my father died. He had never got over the death of my mother. He thought that he would die before her, proof that plans do not always work out. He died partly through his alcoholism in a very sad and wasteful way. "A man with so many talents, the short sleep of time melting into the long sleep of eternity. You died with the purity and innocence of your childhood upon you, though you died in your grey hairs."*

The period of his illness was one of intense difficulty and upset in my life. His death brings a sense of release, of moving on; and also becoming aware of your my mortality.

During that period there were people who played a very supportive role and continue to do so. They are my family, Christine Lewis, and some very special friends Catherine Sunter, Kim and Dermot Walters. Real friends who warm you by their presence, and you trust with your secrets. Others gave time, hugs and understanding. They have not been forgotten.

S Lewis. Barnoldswick, May 2003.

* *The Story Of An African Farm. Olive Schreiner.*
Publisher Oxford World's Classics.